The Institute of Biology's
Studies in Biology no. 1

Ecological Energetics

by John Phillipson, B.Sc., Ph.D., F.I.Biol.
Reader in Animal Ecology, University of Oxford

Edward Arnold (Publishers) Ltd

First published 1966
by Edward Arnold (Publishers) Limited,
25 Hill Street
London, W1X 8LL
Reprinted 1967
Reprinted 1968
Reprinted 1969
Reprinted 1970 (twice)
Reprinted 1971
Reprinted 1972

Board edition: ISBN 0 7131 2078 9
Paper edition: ISBN 0 7131 2079 7

Printed offset in Great Britain by
The Camelot Press Ltd, London and Southampton

General Preface to the Series

It is no longer possible for one textbook to cover the whole field of Biology and to remain sufficiently up to date. At the same time students at school, and indeed those in their first year at universities, are unlikely to be able to find the time, or to have the necessary facilities, for consulting a large number of advanced texts and original papers. It is most important, however, for students to be contemporary in their biological outlook and to be aware of the directions in which the most important developments are taking place.

The Biological Education Committee, set up jointly by the Royal Society and the Institute of Biology, is sponsoring, therefore, the production of a series of booklets dealing with limited biological topics in which recent progress has been most rapid and important.

The booklets are written by recognized experts in their own fields, who are interested not only in the subject matter but also in the way in which it is presented to potential biologists as part of their scientific training. An essential feature of the series is that the booklets indicate as clearly as possible the methods that have been employed in elucidating the problems with which they deal. There are suggestions for practical work for the student which will serve to familiarize him with modern techniques and methods, and thus form a sound scientific basis for his understanding.

1966

INSTITUTE OF BIOLOGY
41 Queen's Gate
London, S.W.7.

Preface

This booklet is intended to serve as an introduction to the relatively new subject of Ecological Energetics (Production Biology), and to indicate the general principles on which the subject is based.

The biological capacity of the earth depends ultimately on the energy received from the sun, and man, to satisfy amongst other things his demand for food, depends on the use to which this energy is put by living organisms. With more than two-thirds of the world population undernourished it is of great importance to understand the transformation of solar energy by communities of living organisms, and Ecological Energetics is the study of such transformations.

Durham, 1966   J. P.

Contents

Energy, Energy Conversion, Conservation, and Utilization 1

1.1   Ecology and energetics

Ecology is that branch of science which deals with the relationship between living things and their physical environment together with all the other living organisms within it. Organisms and the physical environment in which they exist form what, for convenience, is termed an ecosystem. Ecology can thus be described as the study of the inter-relationships within ecosystems, or as ODUM (1959) prefers, 'the study of the structure and function of nature'. Energetics in the context of this book is concerned with the energy transformations which occur within ecosystems.

Before examining the ecological aspects of energetics it is necessary to consider the concept of energy, and the laws which govern energy changes.

1.2   Work and energy

Energy is the capacity to do work and various forms of energy are recognized, but those of greatest importance to living organisms are mechanical, chemical, radiant, and heat energy.

Mechanical energy has two forms, kinetic and potential. Kinetic or free energy may be described as 'useful' energy which a body possesses by virtue of its motion, and is measured by the amount of work which is done in bringing the body to rest. Potential energy is stored energy, only potentially useful until its conversion into the kinetic or free form when it becomes available to accomplish work. Conversion from the potential form to the kinetic involves movement.

All organisms must work to live and they therefore require a source of potential energy which can be utilized. This is found in the chemical energy of food. Assemblies of atoms in matter can be rearranged into different groups and thus, by the movement of atoms, chemical energy is liberated. The combustion (oxidation) of coal in a furnace, or of food by respiratory processes, releases energy which can be used to accomplish work. Both illustrate the conversion of chemical to mechanical energy.

The sun, a vast incandescent sphere of gas, releases energy by the nuclear transmutation of hydrogen to helium, and it is upon this energy that life on earth depends. Solar radiation is energy in the form of electromagnetic waves involving a rhythmic exchange between potential and kinetic energy.

Heat is a very special form of energy resulting from the random movement of molecules, which by virtue of their motion possess kinetic energy. It is evolved when all other forms of energy (which exist as a result of non-random movement) are transformed, and work is done. All work, including the growth and reproduction of living organisms, represents the transformation of energy and ultimately involves heat production. For example, when an animal during respiration releases the potential energy of glucose, approximately two-thirds of it is converted into mechanical energy to be used for work (activity and growth), and one-third is given off as heat. There are instances of work where heat is absorbed (endergonic processes); the cooling unit of a refrigerator, and the fixation of atmospheric nitrogen by certain bacteria are examples, but these processes are not self-supporting energetically. The presence of an outside source of energy, derived from an exergonic process, is necessary to drive an endergonic process. Nitrogen fixation, for example, is always accompanied by the exothermic breakdown of organic substances. Heat energy released by an exergonic process is never used with complete efficiency by the endergonic one, and so whenever work is done the trend is always towards heat production. In natural processes, changes of one form of energy to another (except to heat) are normally incomplete because the movement, already shown to be necessary for energy conversions, involves friction and heat production.

1.3   Energy sources

On earth the ultimate source of animal food is plant life, which acts as a potential energy store. But what are the energy sources of plants? Fungi, many bacteria, and a few flowering plants, for example Venus' Fly Trap, have food requirements similar to animals and utilize organic matter with a high potential energy, obtained from the tissues of other organisms. Animals and plants which obtain their food in this way are referred to collectively as heterotrophs. All other organisms are autotrophs. These are independent of outside sources of organic materials, and manufacture their own from inorganic chemicals with the aid of energy absorbed from the environment. A few bacteria, many blue-green algae, and all green plants are autotrophs.

The energy used by *Beggiatoa*, a blue-green alga, in synthesizing organic materials is produced by oxidation processes. Hydrogen sulphide is oxidized to elementary sulphur which is deposited within the cells:

$$2H_2S + O_2 \rightarrow 2H_2O + 2S + 126 \text{ energy units (kcal)}$$

When the hydrogen sulphide is exhausted the sulphur is further oxidized to sulphate:

$$O_2 + \tfrac{2}{3}S + \tfrac{2}{3}H_2O \rightarrow \tfrac{2}{3}SO_4 + \tfrac{4}{3}H + 98 \text{ energy units (kcal)}$$

The energy released is used to reduce carbon dioxide to bioorganic substances, the overall equation being:

$$6H_2 + 2O_2 + CO_2 + energy \rightarrow (CH_2O) + 5H_2O$$

Beggiatoa is thus able to grow in the complete absence of organic substances, its energy source being the low potential chemical energy of
inorganic materials. Autotrophs utilizing materials with a low potential
chemical energy as their energy source are said to be chemo-autotrophic,
or chemosynthetic.

The vast majority of autotrophs, however, possess the green pigment
chlorophyll and, in its presence, providing that a source of radiant energy
is available, organic material can be synthesized from water and carbon
dioxide. This process is known as photosynthesis:

$$6CO_2 + 6H_2O + light\ energy \rightarrow C_6H_{12}O_6 + 6O_2$$

The extent to which chemosynthetic autotrophs are an important
source of food for heterotrophs is not known, but it is generally assumed
that their contribution is insignificant compared with that of photosynthetic plants. Photosynthetic plants may thus be considered the
major source of food, and hence energy for heterotrophs.

1.4   The laws governing energy transformations

All forms of energy are inter-convertible, and when conversions occur
they do so according to rigorous laws of exchange. These are the laws of
thermodynamics.

The First Law of Thermodynamics is also known as the Law of
Conservation of Energy. In the present context the most useful definition
of this law is that

*Energy may be transformed from one form into another but is
neither created nor destroyed.*

Thus when a change of any kind occurs in a closed system (where the
amount of matter is fixed but energy is able to enter or leave) an increase
or decrease occurs in the internal energy (E) of the system itself, heat (Q)
is evolved or absorbed, and work (W) is done, therefore

$$\Delta E \qquad = \qquad Q \qquad + \qquad W$$

the decrease in	the heat	the work done
internal energy	given off by	by the system
of the system	the system	

where the Greek symbol delta (Δ) signifies the change in quantity.

The First Law of Thermodynamics includes the more specific Law of
Constant Heat Sums which is of great importance to biologists interested

in energy transformations. It states that the total amount of heat produced or absorbed if a chemical reaction is carried out in stages is equal
to the total amount of heat evolved or consumed when the reaction occurs
directly. A good biological example is the oxidation of glucose to carbon
dioxide and water.

1. Direct reaction (combustion)

$$C_6H_{12}O_6 + 6O_2 \rightarrow 6H_2O + 6CO_2 + 673 \text{ energy units (kcal)}$$

2. Two-stage reaction (fermentation)

(a) $C_6H_{12}O_6 \qquad \rightarrow 2C_2H_5OH + 2CO_2 + \quad 18 \text{ energy units (kcal)}$

(b) $2C_2H_5OH + 6O_2 \rightarrow \qquad 6H_2O \quad + 4CO_2 + 655 \text{ energy units (kcal)}$

(a)+(b) $C_6H_{12}O_6 \quad + 6O_2 \rightarrow \qquad 6H_2O \quad + 6CO_2 + 673 \text{ energy units (kcal)}$

Thus no matter what pathway a particular reaction follows the total
amount of heat evolved or absorbed is always the same.

The First Law of Thermodynamics recognizes the interconvertibility
of all forms of energy but does not predict how complete the conversions
will be. As we have seen, all energy transformations, except the transformations to heat, are incomplete. The reason for this lies in the very
nature of heat, which is a property of molecules moving about at random.
By contrast, all other forms of energy result from an ordered, non-
random arrangement of the elementary particles of matter. PORTER (1965)
has pointed out that disorder is the natural condition because an ordered
arrangement conforms to a prechosen requirement and, since heat is the
only form of energy due to disorder, or random movement, it is therefore
the most likely energy to appear.

The Second Law of Thermodynamics is directly concerned with the
conversion of all forms of energy to heat, and the most useful definition
for students of ecological energetics is that

> Processes involving energy transformations will not occur spon-
> taneously unless there is a degradation of energy from a non-random
> to a random form.

1.5   The calorie and other energy units

Progress in the study of energy and energy transformation is limited
without a means of measurement. In the eighteenth century it was found
that potential energy could be readily measured by the simple multi-
plication, Weight Lifted × Height Raised. The work done in raising a one
gram weight against the force of gravity to a height of one centimetre is
981 ergs, and ten million (10^7) ergs are referred to as one joule.

About the same time heat was first measured with accuracy, in terms
of the rise in temperature when the heat was absorbed by a specified mass

of water, thus Heat Energy = Mass of Water × Rise in Temperature. The amount of heat required to raise the temperature of one gram of water through one degree centigrade ($14 \cdot 5°C$ to $15 \cdot 5°C$) is termed a calorie (cal) and one thousand calories (10^3) constitute a kilogram-calorie (kcal or Cal). Each form of energy has its own unit of measurement, but if different forms of energy are to be compared it is necessary to know the relationships of the various units to one another. A direct link between mechanical and heat energy was not discovered until the mid-nineteenth century when Joule determined the mechanical equivalent of heat and showed that $4 \cdot 2 \times 10^7$ ergs are equivalent to one calorie (or $4 \cdot 2$ joules = 1 calorie). Chemical energy can also be measured in heat units by means of a bomb-calorimeter. A known weight of a substance under test is completely combusted in an insulated metal container and by measuring the quantity of heat produced in the bomb-calorimeter the calorific value of the substance is calculated. Because all forms of energy can be converted completely to heat, but not completely to any other form, the calorie is especially useful for comparative purposes. Ecological energetics which is the study of energy transfer, and energy transformations from one form to another within ecosystems, uses the calorie, or kilogram-calorie, as its basic unit of measurement.

1.6 Energy transformations in nature

The ecologist interested in energetics is primarily concerned with the quantity of incident energy per unit area of the ecosystem and the efficiency with which this energy is converted by organisms into other forms.

An overall impression of ecosystem energetics can be obtained by studying the efficiency with which all the autotrophs in an ecosystem convert solar energy to the chemical energy of plant protoplasm, and the efficiency with which this is utilized by all the heterotrophs. On the other hand studies can be restricted to particular plant and animal species, thereby giving an insight into the part played by key species in facilitating energy flow within ecosystems.

The quantity of solar energy entering the earth's atmosphere is approximately $15 \cdot 3 \times 10^8$ cal/m²/yr. Much of this is scattered by dust particles, or is used in the evaporation of water. The average amount of radiant energy per unit area per unit time actually available to plants varies with geographical location, but in Britain the figure is of the order of $2 \cdot 5 \times 10^8$ cal/m²/yr; in Michigan, U.S.A., $4 \cdot 7 \times 10^8$ cal/m²/yr; and in Georgia, U.S.A., $6 \cdot 0 \times 10^8$ cal/m²/yr. As much as 95 to 99 per cent of this energy is immediately lost from the plants in the form of sensible heat and heat of evaporation. The remaining 1 to 5 per cent is used in photosynthesis and is transformed into the chemical energy of plant tissues.

The synthesis of plant materials by autotrophs is designated primary production, and the total amount of chemical energy stored by them per unit area per unit time is referred to as the gross primary productivity, or the gross primary production. Gross primary production does not, however, represent the food potentially available to heterotrophs. Autotrophs in synthesizing organic matter must perform work, and the energy for this is obtained from the break down (oxidation) of organic substances in the process of respiration. Gross primary production minus respiration therefore represents the food energy potentially available to heterotrophs, and is designated net primary production. In nature net primary production is normally between 80 and 90 per cent of the gross primary production. Figure 1–1 shows the results obtained by GOLLEY (1960) for the utilization of solar energy by the perennial grass-herb vegetation of an old-field community in Michigan, U.S.A.

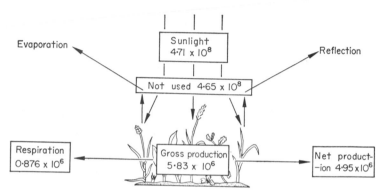

Fig. 1–1   The fate of solar energy incident upon the perennial grass-herb vegetation of an old-field community in Michigan, U.S.A. All measurements in cal/m²/yr. (From data in GOLLEY, 1960.)

The transformation of solar energy to chemical energy by plants thus conforms with the laws of thermodynamics:

Solar energy   = Chemical energy   + Heat energy
assimilated by   of growth of plant(s)   of
plant(s)   (including seeds, exudates, etc.)   respiration

In general, plant organic matter does not accumulate from year to year (one exception is peat deposition), and presumably a dynamic equilibrium exists between the net primary production of plants and the amount of food assimilated by heterotrophs. Individual heterotrophs do not assimilate all of the food they consume. In herbivores as much as 90 per cent of the total food intake may not be assimilated and may pass out of the body as faeces. In carnivores as much as 75 per cent of the food eaten may be assimilated (PHILLIPSON, 1960b), although 30 to 50 per cent is more normal. Thus according to the laws of thermodynamics we can state for a heterotroph:

Chemical energy	=	Chemical energy	+	Chemical energy
eaten by		assimilated by		of faeces produced
heterotroph(s)		heterotrophs(s)		by heterotroph(s)

and

Chemical energy	=	Chemical energy of	+	Heat energy
assimilated by		growth of heterotrophs		of respiration
heterotroph(s)		(including production		
		of young and excretory		
		products)		

The storage of energy in heterotroph tissues is termed secondary production in contrast to the primary production of autotrophs. Faeces and body tissues of heterotrophs eventually serve as food material for other heterotrophs. At each transfer of energy heat is evolved. The end result conforms with the laws of thermodynamics and may be expressed:

Solar energy entering the system = Heat energy leaving the system

Our interest lies in what happens to the energy after it enters the system and before it leaves it. The effective running of ecological systems depends upon the transfer of energy from organism to organism, and energy transfers of this type constitute the food chains which we shall consider in the next chapter.

Food Webs and Trophic Levels 2

2.1 Food chains

It is clear that a plant may be eaten by one animal which, in its turn, is eaten by another, and this creature may itself be eaten by yet a third animal and so on. Such a sequence of events is termed a food chain.

In the open sea the plants carrying out photosynthesis are free floating microscopic green algae; principally diatoms and flagellates. Amongst the many animals which utilize these plants as food is a small crustacean known as *Calanus finmarchicus*. This copepod crustacean is an important item in the diet of adult herrings, and thus we can write the simple food chain:

Chaetoceros decipiens (a diatom) → *Calanus finmarchicus* (a copepod)
→ *Clupea harengus* (herring)

Diatoms also form the basis of some food chains in fresh water habitats; for example the diatom *Navicula viridula*, along with other species, forms an algal slime on rocks and boulders in brooks and streams. This diatom may be grazed by the larva of the may fly *Baetis rhodani*, which in turn may be eaten by the caddis fly larvae, *Rhyacophila* sp. We can represent this food chain as:

Navicula viridula (a diatom) → *Baetis rhodani* (a mayfly)
→ *Rhyacophila* sp. (caseless caddis)

On land macroscopic vegetation is the most obvious source of food for heterotrophs. The grass *Festuca ovina* will serve as an example of such a solar energy trap. *Microtus agrestis* (the short-tailed field vole) can exploit *Festuca* as a food source, and in its turn become a meal for the weasel (*Mustela mustela*). Hence:

Festuca ovina (a grass) → *Microtus agrestis* (a vole)
→ *Mustela* (the weasel)

These three food chains have a number of features in common, each consists of three steps, they are all linear relationships, and the generalized expression

Plant → Herbivore → Carnivore

is applicable.

2.2 Food webs

In nature, the food and feeding relationships of plants and animals are rarely, if ever, as simple as the examples of food chains quoted above.

The complexity of these feeding relationships can be readily illustrated by considering, in greater detail, the *Chaetoceros → Calanus → Clupea* chain already mentioned. Clearly the copepod will feed on a wide variety of species of both diatoms and flagellates. Similarly the copepod *Calanus*, although it forms some 21 per cent of an adult herring's diet, is eaten by organisms other than herring; for example it forms 70 per cent of the diet of larval sand eels (*Ammodytes* spp.), which themselves account for 40 per cent of the adult herring's diet (see FRASER, 1962).

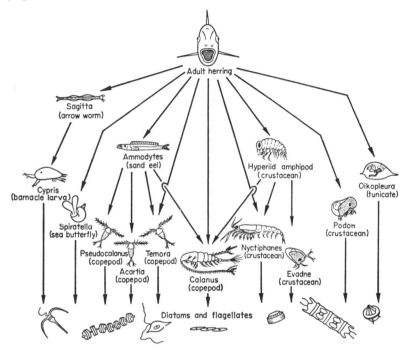

Fig. 2–1   The feeding relationships of adult herring. (Based on HARDY, 1924 and 1959; courtesy of Collins.)

Figure 2–1, based on the work of HARDY (1924), shows the complexity of the feeding relationships of an adult herring. It is clear that the simple food chain we started with is not an isolated linear system but inter-connects with a large number of other food chains. This interconnection leads to the food relationships of organisms being thought of, and expressed diagrammatically, as a web, and thus we refer to the complex situation as a *food web* rather than a food chain. It is obvious that more than three links may be involved in a food chain and thus the generalized expression plant → herbivore → carnivore must be expanded to plant → herbivore → carnivore$_1$ → carnivore$_2$ - - - → carnivore$_n$. ELTON (1927) realized that there was an upper limit to the number of links in any one food chain, and pointed out that this number rarely exceeds five. Such a food chain can be seen by referring once more to the food web of the herring. Bearing in mind that the herring may be eaten by a sea bird, for example the Shag (*Phalacrocorax aristotelis*), we can write:

$$Chaetoceros \rightarrow Calanus \rightarrow Ammodytes \rightarrow Clupea \rightarrow Phalacrocorax$$

(Plant)　　　　(Herbivore)　　(Carnivore$_1$)　　(Carnivore$_2$)　　(Carnivore$_3$)

The food web illustrated in Figure 2–1 was constructed to show those organisms which form, either directly or indirectly, part of the diet of the adult herring; and if one introduced all the organisms encountered in the herring's environment, then the web would become extremely complex. The discovery and description of a food web in any given habitat is an enormous task.

2.3   Tracing food chains and food webs

A number of different methods have been employed in determining food chains and food webs. In some instances straightforward observation will suffice as a first approximation. For example we can see that certain aphids are restricted to certain species of plant, we can also see that many of these aphids are eaten by ladybird larvae. However, the aphids may also be eaten by a small bird which may itself be taken by a hawk. Clearly observation is unsatisfactory in that one is never certain whether all possible links in the food web have been observed. A second approach is to collect from a given habitat representatives of all the species occurring in that habitat and to analyse their gut contents. Provided that a large enough number of individuals of each species is examined it is possible to state, with some certainty, which animals feed upon what. Gut analyses require that the investigator be well versed in the naming of species not only as whole organisms but also from their separate parts. Although it is possible to identify hard parts such as plant epidermis, diatom cases, and the skeletal elements of various animals, how is one to identify plant juices, animal body fluids, and animals without hard skeletal elements? Assuming that this could be done, it must be remembered that the fluids and soft tissues are more readily digested than the harder elements and may be eaten and assimilated so rapidly that they would rarely appear as items in a diet.

Recently methods have been employed which overcome some of the objections raised in connection with gut analyses. DEMPSTER (1960) studied the predators of the broom beetle *Phytodecta olivacea* using the precipitin test. In this case caged rabbits were inoculated with a cell-free extract of the broom beetle; as might be expected antibodies were produced in the blood serum of the rabbit. Some 50 ml of blood were drawn from each rabbit, blood cells, and lipids, were removed and the resulting serum sterilized, freeze dried, and stored. Following the production of the antiserum a sample of the possible predators of the broom beetle were brought into the laboratory and identified. Smears of these animals were made by crushing either the whole animal or its gut contents on filter paper, and drying it rapidly over phosphorus pentoxide, the smears were extracted for 24 h in normal saline, centrifuged, and the clear supernatant liquids used for testing. The test was made by drawing a small volume (0·02 ml) of the extracts into a series of capillary tubes, followed by an equal volume of antiserum which had been reconstituted with distilled water. After a period of 2 h at room temperature the tubes were examined; the presence of *Phytodecta* in the meal was shown by the formation of a white precipitate of antigen and antibody at the interface of the two liquids. By this method ten predator species were shown to feed regularly on the broom beetle.

It may be thought that such a method is tedious, but it must be noted that even when a prey animal possesses an exoskeleton it may not be identifiable in gut analyses. This point is well illustrated by the work of Reynoldson and his colleagues (REYNOLDSON and YOUNG, 1963; YOUNG, MORRIS, and REYNOLDSON, 1964). Analysis of the gut contents of the flatworm *Dendrocoelum lacteum* suggested that its main food item in nature was oligochaet worms, which were identified by the presence of undigested setae in the gut. However, laboratory experiments showed that *Asellus* (the water-hoglouse) was eaten in preference to oligochaet worms, although only the body fluids and soft tissues were ingested. The apparent paradox was resolved by carrying out precipitin tests on freshly caught *Dendrocoelum*. A rabbit anti-*Asellus* serum used in conjunction with *Dendrocoelum* smears showed without doubt that this flatworm fed extensively upon the water-hoglouse in nature.

A fourth method which has been used in tracing the feeding relationships of various organisms utilizes radioactive isotopes. ODUM and KUENZLER (1963) applied this technique in studying a terrestrial food chain. Phosphorus-32 was used to 'label' a number of individuals of a single plant species by spraying the foliage. Following the 'labelling' samples of the animals living in the vicinity of the plants were taken at regular intervals, and the amount of P^{32} in each of the animal species assayed. Any animal which showed radioactivity must have been directly, or indirectly, dependent upon the 'labelled' plants for its initial food source. The animals most actively removing material from the plant, as shown by their early peak of radioactivity were the small forms such as the cricket (*Oecanthus*), and the ant (*Dorymyrmex*). Larger herbivores such as the grasshopper (*Melanoplus*) followed these, and finally the predators, such as spiders, which prey on the herbivores reached their peak of radioactivity. Clearly a method which effectively 'labels' the primary food source, and allows the subsequent transfer of this material to be followed, can be of great value in isolating food chains.

2.4   Ecological pyramids

The more knowledge we have about a particular food web the more complex it becomes. Diagrammatic representation grows so complicated that it becomes very difficult to unravel individual links and yet retain an appreciation of the whole system. There is, therefore, a strong case for producing generalized representations, or models, of food webs even after detailed investigations have been made.

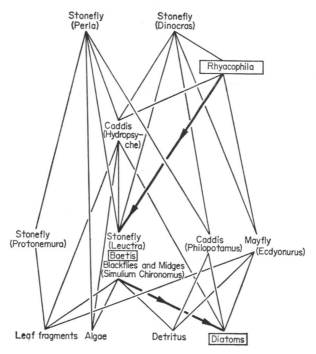

Fig. 2–2   Part of the food web of a fresh water stream in Wales. (Based on JONES, 1949; courtesy of *J. Anim. Ecol.*)

A simplified model for part of a food web in a fresh water stream, which includes our earlier food chain example, *Navicula → Baetis → Rhyacophila*, is given in Figure 2–2. In this figure, based on the work of JONES (1949), animals with similar feeding habits and similar predators have been grouped together. Despite the grouping the model is still complex because of its many interconnecting links. Furthermore it is difficult to compare the food web in one situation with that in another, for different species are involved in each case. However, ELTON (1927) noted that '... the animals at the base of a food chain are relatively abundant while those at the end are relatively few in number, and there is a progressive decrease in between the two extremes'. This *pyramid of numbers,* as it was called, is found in animal communities all over the world, and the widespread occurrence of such a phenomenon provides a common denominator by which different communities may be compared. For general comparative purposes it is permissible to ignore the species composition of food webs and group together those organisms with similar food habits. The generally recognized procedure in constructing a pyramid of numbers is to group and count all of the autotrophs and call them the *primary producers*; then organisms one step away from the primary producers in the food web, that is the herbivores, are grouped, counted, and termed the *primary consumers.* Organisms two and three steps away from the primary producers are similarly treated. These carnivores are called *secondary consumers* and *tertiary consumers* respectively. An alternative nomenclature is producers, herbivores, carnivores,

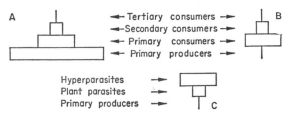

Fig. 2–3   Pyramids of numbers. A, when the primary producers are small; B, when the primary producers are large; C, a plant/parasite food web.

and top carnivores. Figure 2–3 shows diagrammatically the major types of pyramids of numbers that might be expected in nature. In Figure 2–3A the primary producers are small and if they are to support the relatively larger herbivores that feed on them they must be numerous. In Figure 2–3B the primary producers are large, for example trees, and here an individual plant can support many herbivores; however, above the producer level the upright pyramid is apparent. Inverted pyramids of numbers only appear when parasitic food webs are considered. This situation is represented in Figure 2–3C.

The information contained within a pyramid of numbers permits us to state the number of herbivores supported by a given number of plants, and so on. There are attendant difficulties with this approach, however. If we are to compare two different ecosystems by considerng how many animals a given number of plants can support in each system, it is not very informative if we cquate a diatom with a tree, or an elephant with a vole. This difficulty has been partially overcome by using the weight (biomass) of organisms rather than their numbers. If this procedure is

2

followed, the resulting structure is termed a *pyramid of biomass*. Examples are given in Fig. 2–4. Two forms of pyramids of biomass can be constructed. If producers support herbivores, and herbivores support carnivores, then the upright pyramid of biomass is the one we might expect, for how can a lower weight of producers give rise to a greater weight of consumers? However, the pyramid of biomass for the English Channel suggests that this may happen. Fortunately this apparent paradox can be readily explained.

The data for the construction of pyramids of numbers and biomass are collected by sampling the flora and fauna and the numbers and/or weights of the different feeding types ascertained. These results are then expressed for example as numbers per acre, or weight per cubic metre. From this information the appropriate pyramid is constructed. But the sampling period is of limited duration, it may have lasted for several minutes in the case of sampling microscopic algae, or a week or so if

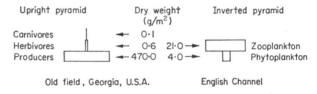

Fig. 2–4   Pyramids of biomass. An upright pyramid for an old-field in Georgia, U.S.A., and an inverted pyramid for the English Channel. (From ODUM, 1959; courtesy of W. B. Saunders, Philadelphia.)

sampling a forest. Thus pyramids of numbers and biomass only indicate the amount of material present over a very short period of time. The amount of material present at any one instant in time is known as the *standing crop*, and gives no indication of the total amount of material produced or the rate at which that material is being produced. A simple example will clarify this point. We all know that many trees may live one hundred years or more, we also know that many microscopic algae live for a few days only. Both plants must reproduce if the species to which they belong is to survive, yet a tree may take six years to produce its first seeds whereas a microscopic alga may take less than a day to reproduce itself. Thus, a five-year-old tree may be still growing without having seeded while a microscopic alga may have given rise to millions of offspring in the same period, the total weight of which equals or exceeds that of the tree. An estimate of the standing crop of trees is a measurement of organic materials that have accumulated over a long period of time, whereas an estimate of the standing crop of algae is a measurement of organic materials accumulated over a very short period. In neither case has the rate of accumulation been taken into account. Clearly, production rate (productivity) rather than standing crop is the important feature when studying the functioning of ecosystems.

Pyramids of numbers and biomass therefore have their limitations. They inform us of the quantity of organic material present at any one moment but give no indication of process rates (turnover time).

If we return to our earlier examples of pyramids of biomass it will be realized that the total amount of plant material produced per annum in the English Channel far exceeds the amount indicated by the standing crop figure.

A third type of ecological pyramid overcomes many of the objections raised in connection with pyramids of numbers and biomass, this is the *energy pyramid* shown in Figure 2–5 where each bar represents the total amount of energy utilized by the different feeding types in a square metre,

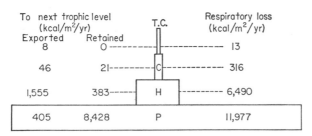

Fig. 2–5 Pyramid of energy for Silver Springs, Florida, U.S.A. (Based on ODUM, 1957; courtesy of *Ecol. Monogr.*)

over a set period of time (one year). This method of expressing data has many advantages and overcomes the difficulty encountered with a pyramid of numbers where one expresses individual organisms as far apart as daffodils and whales by the same unit, namely 1. It also avoids the difficulty encountered in pyramids of biomass where one might, for example, equate 1 g of the mollusc *Ensis* (calorific value without shell approximately 3,500 cal/g dry wt) with 1 g of the copepod crustacean *Calanus hyperboreus* (approximately 7,400 cal/g dry wt).

From what has been written so far it should be apparent that energy units provide a unifying concept, a means of expressing the productivity of an individual organism or of all of the organisms within an ecosystem. Further, the concept permits comparisons of the productivity of regions as different as desert and tropical forest, or mountain tops and ocean beds.

2.5 The trophic-dynamic aspect

It was not until Lindemann (1942) developed his now classic concept of community dynamics that widespread interest arose in the measurement

of the rate of energy transfer within ecosystems. Figure 2–6 shows
Lindemann's concept in its simplest form. Those organisms with similar
feeding habits have been grouped together, as in an ecological pyramid,
and each grouping, or feeding level, is termed a *trophic level*. The energy
content (standing crop) of any one trophic level is designated by the
Greek capital letter lambda (Λ). In an ecosystem, however, there is more
than one trophic level, and so a subscript is employed to indicate which
of the trophic levels is being referred to; hence Λ_1, represents producers,
Λ_2 herbivores, and so on. In general terms, Λ_n is taken to indicate any

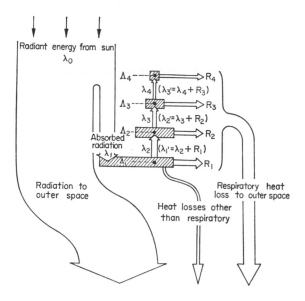

Fig. 2–6   A diagrammatic representation of the LINDEMANN (1942) concept
of community dynamics.

one of these levels; thus if Λ_n is applied to the herbivores then Λ_{n-1}
signifies the producers, and Λ_{n+1} the carnivores.

Considering any trophic level Λ_n we know that energy is continuously
entering and leaving it; in other words there is a functional, or trophic-
dynamic, aspect to the ecosystem as well as a descriptive or structural one.
In the same way that we can refer to the standing crop of any trophic
level by the symbol Λ_n so can we designate the contribution of energy
per unit time from Λ_{n-1} to Λ_n by little lambda (λ_n). Because of work
done by the organisms constituting Λ_n a proportion of the energy they
receive (λ_n) is dissipated as heat. This loss of heat energy per unit time
(R) plus the energy (λ_{n+1}) passed per unit time to the next trophic level
(Λ_{n+1}) is symbolized as $\lambda_{n'}$. Thus $\lambda_{2'}$ represents the heat loss per unit

time from $\Lambda_2(R_2)$ plus the potential energy passed on to Λ_3, namely λ_3.

Following Lindemann's nomenclature it is now possible to write a generalized equation expressing the rate of change of the energy content of any trophic level (Λ_n):

$$\frac{\delta \Lambda_n}{\delta t} = \lambda_n + \lambda_{n'}.$$

This is simply a means of stating in mathematical symbols that the rate of change in the energy content of a standing crop is equal to the rate at which energy is absorbed by that standing crop minus the rate at which energy is lost from it. Minus is the correct word to use in the previous sentence for by definition $\lambda_{n'}$ is always negative.

The trophic-dynamic formulation poses a number of important questions. Λ_n, as already stated, represents the energy content of a standing crop of a trophic level; we might ask if Λ_n/Λ_{n-1} is a constant. For example, does Λ_2/Λ_1 in a tropical forest equal Λ_2/Λ_1 in the open ocean? Or, in a desert, does Λ_2/Λ_1 equal Λ_3/Λ_2? More important still is the fact that λ_n represents the net production of a trophic level, and as such is a measure of the energy available to the next highest trophic level. How efficiently is energy transferred between trophic levels? Is λ_n/λ_{n-1}, or as SLOBODKIN (1962) expresses it λ_j/λ_i a constant? Answers to questions such as these are important not only from the academic viewpoint of discovering what basic principles, if any, underlie the functioning of ecosystems, but also as a means of suggesting to man how he might turn the potential productivity of ecosystems to his own use.

2.6   Laboratory studies and ecological efficiency

We have seen that natural ecosystems are complex and that a study of the trophic-dynamic aspect of a complete ecosystem in nature is therefore a formidable task. The situation can be simplified by studying 'laboratory made' ecosystems. This approach is justified if one is primarily interested in ecological theory, and wishes to put forward predictive hypotheses that can be tested by field observations at a later date. The laboratory approach has been followed by SLOBODKIN (1959) and his co-workers in America.

The first of Slobodkin's laboratory ecosystems contained three-species; the producer *Chlamydomonas reinhardi*, the primary consumer *Daphnia pulex*, and the role of secondary consumer was played by the experimenter, *Homo sapiens*. This ecosystem was used in an attempt to decide whether or not there is any constancy in the ratios of the net productivities of a prey organism (λ_i) and the animal using it as food (λ_j). In the *Chlamydomonas/Daphnia/Homo* experiment λ_i is the number of calories of *Chlamydomonas* consumed per unit time by *Daphnia*, and λ_j the number of calories of *Daphnia* 'consumed' per unit time by the experimenter.

Initially the experimental procedure consisted of growing the food supply (*C. reinhardi*) in pure culture on agar plates, and setting up 27 populations of *D. pulex* in 50 ml beakers. The populations were divided into five groups, and each group was given a set ration of food every four days. Group 1 populations were given one ration of food each four days, Group 2 two rations of food, and so on up to Group 5 which received five rations of food per four days. A single ration of food consisted of a fixed volume of *C. reinhardi* culture which, from earlier observations, was known to contain on average 1·53 mg dry wt of *Chlamydomonas* cells. The calorific value of *C. reinhardi*, as determined by bomb-calorimetry, was 5,289 cal/g dry wt, thus one ration of food had a calorific value of 8·1 cals. On the assumption that all of the food given to each *Daphnia* population was eaten, then the calorific value of the food eaten every four days could be calculated. Clearly the value of λ_i was known for each of the laboratory ecosystems.

On each feeding occasion the *Daphnia* population was sampled and the number and lengths of different-sized *Daphnia* determined. Animals of 0·7, 1·3, and 1·88 mm in length were known, from bomb-calorimetry, to have mean calorific values of 4·05, 4·124, and 5·075 kcal/g dry wt respectively; it was thus possible to calculate the total calorific content of each *Daphnia* population. In each of the five experimental groups at least one population was kept as a control, there being no interference other than that caused by feeding and sampling, so that the population size became adjusted to the feeding level. Figure 2–7A shows that in the control populations there was a linear relationship between the energy content of the food consumed and the energy content of the population.

Populations other than the controls were subjected to predation. Man acted as the predator by removing animals from the experimental populations every four days, the number of animals removed being a fixed percentage of the newborn young per four-day period. The number of newborn was easily ascertained from the difference between consecutive population estimates. In some populations only young animals were removed, in others adults; here we shall consider only the adult removal populations. The populations used in the adult removal experiments were those given one, three, and five food rations per four days. Of the four populations fed one food ration per four days, one was subjected to a 25 per cent predation level, and the other three to 50, 75, and 90 per cent predation, respectively. Populations at food levels 3 and 5 were treated in a similar fashion. In all cases the yield to the predator (man) corresponds to λ_j, and so we are now able to study the relationships of the number of calories of *Chlamydomonas* consumed per unit time by *Daphnia* (λ_i) and the yield of *Daphnia* 'consumed' per unit time by man (λ_j).

Because the total *Daphnia* population, and the number of young produced is linearly related to food supply (RICHMAN, 1958), one would expect to find that the highest yield of *Daphnia* would occur at food level 5 and a 90 per cent predation rate; Figure 2–7B shows that, in general, this is so. However, if we consider yield in terms of return per unit food supply per four days, it will be seen from Figure 2–7C that populations

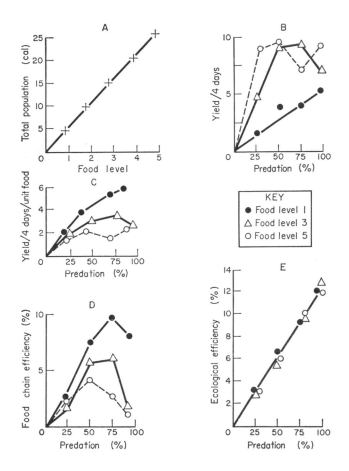

Fig. 2–7   Results of laboratory studies on the ecological efficiency of *Daphnia* populations maintained at different food levels. A, the relationship between the energy content of food consumed and the energy content of the population; B, yield of adult *Daphnia* per 4 days when subjected to different levels of predation; C, yield of adult *Daphnia* per 4 days per unit food supply when subjected to different levels of predation; D, food chain efficiency versus level of predation; E, ecological efficiency versus level of predation. (From data in SLOBODKIN, 1959; courtesy of *Ecology*.)

at food level 1 give the best yield. Does this mean that *Daphnia* populations exploit their food less efficiently at the higher food levels?

The efficiency with which a food supply is exploited by a predator population can be expressed as a percentage by applying the formula

$$\frac{\text{calories of prey, consumed by predator}}{\text{calories of food supplied to prey}} \times \frac{100}{1}$$

This efficiency is termed the *food chain efficiency*. Figure 2–7D shows food chain efficiency plotted against predation rate for each of the *Chlamydomonas/Daphnia*/Man experimental ecosystems. Clearly, above a predation level of 25 per cent the *Daphnia* populations did not exploit their food supply at high food levels as efficiently as they did at the lower ones. It was soon discovered that this lower efficiency was due to the fact that the *Daphnia* remaining in the population after a certain predation rate (25 per cent in the case of food level 5, and 50 per cent and 75 per cent in the case of food levels 3 and 1, respectively) were not sufficiently numerous to consume all the algae supplied. The populations were being 'overfished', that is, they were subject to too intense a predation for maximum food chain efficiency. A maximum food chain efficiency implies, of course, that the food of the prey is being exploited to the best advantage by the predator.

There is a point where yield to a predator is such that the remaining prey population can just consume all of the available food and thus the food chain efficiency will be at a maximum. However, we are now considering a special case of the ratio

$$\frac{\text{calories of prey consumed by the predator}}{\text{calories of food supplied to prey}}$$

for food supplied is equivalent to food consumed, and so we can write:

$$\frac{\text{calories of prey consumed by predator}}{\text{calories of food consumed by prey}} \times \frac{100}{1}$$

This ratio is called the *gross ecological efficiency* and is equivalent to λ_j/λ_i.

In *Chlamydomonas/Daphnia*/Man ecosystems it was possible to estimate the calorific content of the food actually consumed by the *Daphnia*, and hence the gross ecological efficiency. The results are shown in Figure 2–7E, and it is obvious that the difference in the efficiency with which *Daphnia* populations, at different food levels, exploit their food supplies disappear so long as those populations are large enough to consume all of the food supplied. It is apparent also that in this 'laboratory ecosystem' the maximum gross ecological efficiency attainable is of the order of 13 per cent.

As stated previously, a maximum food chain efficiency implies that the food of the prey is being exploited to the best advantage by a predator; but the highest food chain efficiencies are reached when all of the prey's food is consumed, that is when food chain efficiency equals gross ecological efficiency. We can therefore substitute gross ecological efficiency for food chain efficiency in the above statement. The question remains as to whether a figure approximating to 13 per cent is the most likely gross ecological efficiency for all ecosystems, both man made and natural.

SLOBODKIN (1962, 1964) working with an *Artemia* (brine shrimp)/ *Hydra oligactis*/Man laboratory ecosystem showed the maximum gross ecological efficiency of the *Hydra* population to be approximately 7 per cent, and suggests that in natural ecosystems the most probable value for gross ecological efficiency is of the order of 10 per cent. The implication is that in natural ecosystems λ_j/λ_i is a constant and has a value of approximately 10 per cent. We shall consider this aspect in Chapter 3 when data for energy flow in natural ecosystems have been presented.

Grazers and Detritus Feeders in the Ecosystem

3.1 Field studies and ecological efficiency

TEAL (1957) made one of the early attempts at a functional analysis of energy flow in a natural ecosystem. Earlier studies had been made (JUDAY, 1940; LINDEMANN, 1942; ODUM and ODUM, 1955; and ODUM, 1957), but the ecosystem studied by Teal is most like a 'laboratory ecosystem', and therefore is a very useful example of a general method of approach to energy flow studies.

The study area, in Massachusetts, U.S.A., consisted of a small spring approximately 2 m in diameter and 10 to 20 cm deep, and was therefore little larger than a 'laboratory ecosystem'.

The bottom of the spring was covered by mud in which most of the organisms dwelt, for like most springs there was no true plankton. The flora was simple, consisting of diatoms, filamentous green algae, colonial green algae, and the duckweed *Lemna minor*. The fauna was similarly relatively simple, and although forty species were identified, few occurred in numbers and sizes large enough to be important in terms of energy flow. The most abundant animals belonged to the following genera:

DETRITUS FEEDERS

Limnodrilus sp. (oligochaet worm), *Asellus* sp. (isopod crustacean), *Crangonyx* sp. (amphipod crustacean), *Pisidium* sp. (lamellibranch mollusc), *Physa* sp. (gastropod mollusc), and *Calopsectra* sp. (midge larva).

FEEDERS ON LARGER PIECES OF VEGETATION

Frenesia spp. (2), and *Limnophilis* sp. (larvae of caddis flies).

PREDATORS

Anatopynia sp. (midge larva), and two species of *Phagocata* (turbellarian flat worm).

Here is a field situation scarcely more complex than a 'laboratory ecosystem', small, of constant temperature, and with few (12) important animal species.

In Teal's study no measurements were made of the amount of light energy assimilated by the plant materials which formed the herbivore food source. In fact the net production of autotrophs within the spring was of minor importance as a source of energy for the herbivores, because most of the plant material which formed their food was manufactured elsewhere and entered the spring as leaves, fruit, and branches of terrestrial vegetation. An estimate of the energy entering the ecosystem as debris, as well as measurements of the gross production by the flora, was necessary before an overall estimate of the energy entering the ecosystem as plant material could be made.

Gross production of the autotrophs was measured by a modified version of the light- and dark-bottle method (see ODUM, 1963). Glass cylinders 17 cm in diameter were pushed into the bottom mud whilst their tops remained some 2 to 4 cm above the water surface. They were then filled to the top with spring water and covered with an airtight seal. The oxygen content of the water within the cylinders was measured by means of the standard Winkler technique (see DOWDESWELL, 1959) at the beginning and end of a 24 h period. Following these measurements each cylinder was enclosed in a black box to prevent photosynthesis, and the oxygen content of the water was again measured at the beginning and end of a set period. The results from the light and dark cylinders can be used to calculate the amount of oxygen evolved by photosynthesis, and the gross productivity can then be calculated and expressed as $cal/m^2/yr$. Summation of the monthly figures for photosynthesis gave a figure for gross production by the autotrophs of 710 $kcal/m^2/yr$. Autotroph respiration was not measured directly but estimated at 55 $kcal/m^2/yr$, thus the net production of autotrophs within the spring was equivalent to 655 $kcal/m^2/yr$. Wooden trays placed beside the spring to catch falling terrestrial plant debris revealed that 2,350 $kcal/m^2/yr$ entered the ecosystem in this form. Thus a total of 3,005 kcal of plant material entered each square metre of the spring in the year of study. Further measurements showed that plant material amounting to 706 $kcal/m^2/yr$ was not utilized immediately by the herbivores but deposited in the ecosystem; therefore 2,300 $kcal/m^2/yr$ were consumed by the herbivores, this figure is a measure of λ_2.

In addition to establishing the amount of energy taken in by the herbivores over a period of one year it was important to discover the use to which this energy was put. What proportion, if any, went to increase the overall standing crop of herbivores? How much was passed on to carnivores? Was the remainder dissipated as heat of respiration? To answer these questions it was necessary to determine the number, biomass, mortality, moulting losses, and respiratory rate of each of the principal animal species.

Population estimates were obtained by taking random samples of the bottom mud each month. A sampler taking a known sample size was used and each sample was hand sorted under a magnifying lens so that the animals could be counted, weighed, and expressed as numbers or weight per m^2. The calorific values of the different species were determined by a chemical process (IVLEV, 1934). Miniature bomb-calorimeters which combust quantities as small as 5 mg dry wt are now available (SLOBODKIN and RICHMAN, 1960; and PHILLIPSON, 1964). Knowing the calorific values of the various species it was a simple matter to express each month's crop in calories rather than grammes. Table 1 shows population sizes per m^2 for one of the herbivores, the midge larva *Calopsectra dives*.

Table 1   Population of larval, and emerging adults, of *Calopsectra dives* in Root Spring, Concord, Mass., in 1965. (After TEAL, 1957; courtesy of *Ecol. Monogr.*)

	Jan.	Feb.	Mar.	Apr.	May	June	July	Aug.	Sept.	Oct.	Nov.
Larvae											
Number/m^2	0	0	0	0	1,700	89,500	65,000	57,000	200	0	0
kcal/m^2	0	0	0	0	2·1	40·4	56·8	87·6	0·1	0	0
Adults											
Number/m^2	0	0	0	0	13	170	953	3,464	13,250	533	
kcal/m^2	0	0	0	0	0·019	0·246	1·38	5·0	19·3	0·775	

It can be seen that the larval standing crop grew from zero in April up to a maximum of 87·6 kcal/m^2 in August, only to fall to zero again in October. Thus the energy change in the standing crop over the year was nil, and therefore none of the energy consumed by *Calopsectra* was used to increase the overall standing crop of this midge. Table 1 shows that some of the larvae developed into adults which emigrated from the spring on emergence. A measure of the energy leaving the spring as adult midges was obtained by using special traps to catch them as they emerged and converting their biomass into cal/m^2.

The monthly estimates of larval standing crop, which failed to include the production of adult tissues, did not account either for the energy built into the larval skins that were cast or the bodies of larvae that died between consecutive sampling occasions. The number of calories deposited in the spring as cast skins was estimated after laboratory investigations had been made of moulting larvae, and the calorific content of the larvae dying in each month was calculated from field population data.

A measure of the energy dissipated as heat of respiration was also necessary before an annual energy balance sheet could be constructed for *Calopsectra*. Oxygen consumption was determined by placing the larvae in a 20 ml syringe filled with spring water. The oxygen content of the water was measured at the beginning of the experiment with a micro-Winkler technique (FOX and WINGFIELD, 1938). After the syringe and its contents had remained submerged in the spring for 1–3 h the oxygen content was again measured. The difference between the two oxygen determinations gave the oxygen consumption of the larvae within the syringe, and this figure was converted to mg of oxygen per g of larvae per unit time. Finally, oxygen consumption was converted to calories by means of the oxy-calorific equivalent where each mg of oxygen represents a heat loss of 3·38 cal.

It was now possible to estimate the monthly respiratory heat losses of (1) the standing crop, (2) the larval exoskeletons before they were moulted, and (3) the larvae which lived for a time after one sampling occasion but died before the next one. Table 2 summarizes the results for *Calopsectra*.

The net change in standing crop over the year was nil. The heat loss due to respiration amounted to 389·6 kcal/m²/yr, and this plus the calorific value of the total amount of tissue produced equals the amount of energy assimilated by the *Calopsectra* population (520·3 kcal/m²/yr).

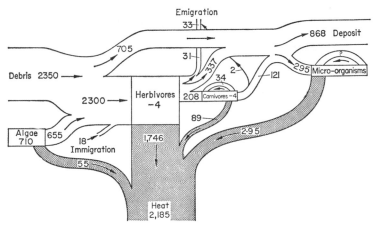

Fig. 3–1   Energy flow diagram for Root Spring, Concord, Mass., in 1953–54. Figures in kcal/m²/yr, numbers inside boxes indicate changes in standing crops. (From TEAL, 1957; courtesy of *Ecol. Monogr.*)

By adopting procedures similar to these Teal constructed energy balance sheets for all the principal species of the spring fauna.

The rates of respiration of the mud-dwelling micro-organisms were also obtained. This was achieved by subtracting the calculated rates of respiration of the known average biomass of macrofauna from the total respiration of the fauna as determined in the light, and dark, cylinder experiments.

With the information now available it was possible to construct an energy flow diagram for the whole ecosystem. Such a diagram is shown in Figure 3–1. Note that the kcal/m²/yr inside the boxes do not represent standing crops, the figure for algae represents gross production over the year whereas the figures for herbivores and carnivores indicate the net change in standing crop. Clearly, the standing crop of both herbivores

Table 2 Balance sheet for energy flow in *Calopsectra dives* in Root Spring, Concord, Mass., in kcal/m². Column 4 shows the calories respired before moulting by the biomass represented in the deposited larval skins. (After TEAL (1957); courtesy of *Ecol. Monogr.*)

Month	Standing crop	Respiration of standing crop	Respiration of animals that died	Respiration of deposit	Emergence	Pupal deposit	Larval deposit	Mortality
October to April	—	—	—	—	—	—	—	—
May	2·1	3·5	—	—	0·02	0·01	—	—
June	40·4	67·5	0·6	3·3	0·25	0·11	4·0	0·7
July	56·8	96·0	1·0	4·8	1·38	0·61	5·7	1·2
August	87·6	146·2	12·4	7·3	5·00	2·2	8·8	14·9
September	0·1	0·2	45·8	—	19·30	8·5	—	54·8
October	—	—	1·8	—	0·78	0·34	—	2·1
	—	312·6	61·6	15·4	26·7	11·8	18·5	73·7

and carnivores at the end of the year was slightly lower than at the beginning. An estimate of the change in the standing crop of micro-organisms was not obtained, neither were these organisms referred to any of the trophic levels.

It is of major importance that of the 2,300 kcal/m²/yr consumed by the herbivores, only 655 kcal were produced within the ecosystem, the remainder entered from outside as debris. Further, of the 3,078 kcal/m²/yr entering the spring 2,185 kcal were dissipated as heat, 33 kcal were lost remainder was deposited within the deposit would be washed out of the spring would have gradually filled

flow through a natural ecosystem we ictive hypothesis that gross ecological er cent. In this instance λ_2 equals ;08 kcal/m²/yr; the gross ecological sed as a percentage, is equivalent to ears then that the prediction of gross aboratory experimentation applies to stem. We must now consider whether ble.

ns the one studied by Teal was very amount of work. Detailed studies of y years of work by an individual, or workers over a shorter period. ODUM in a study of the trophic structure and lorida. The results of this investigation ow diagram reproduced in Figure 3–2. Springs is more comprehensive than for nount of light energy incident upon and estimated, and with the more complex carnivores and top carnivores. In these calculate the gross ecological efficiencies es, which were 11·4 per cent (λ_3/λ_2), and These values are similar to the predicted

of the producers has not been calculated. ent use of λ_n by LINDEMANN (1942). For $_1$ and according to Lindemann represents uction (this is not the same as the energy is for all trophic levels above the producers In Figure 2–6 contrary to Lindemann's tency, λ_1 was taken to represent the energy rocedure follows ENGLEMANN (1961). With ary within the confines of this book to

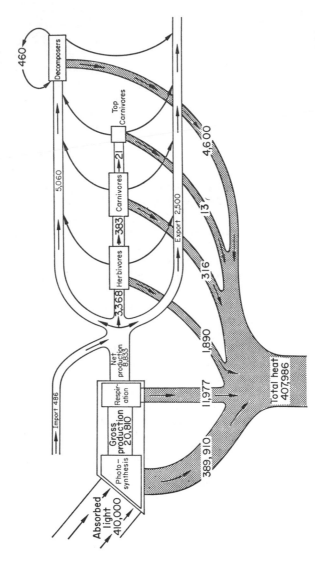

Fig. 3-2 Energy flow diagram for Silver Springs, Florida. Figures in kcal/m²/yr. (Adapted from ODUM, 1957; courtesy of *Ecol. Monogr.*)

restrict the term gross ecological efficiency to animal groups. The few ecological efficiencies so far determined for natural systems range from 5 to 30 per cent. More field data are necessary before a final decision about the constancy of λ_j/λ_i can be made.

3.2 Energy flow models

Comparison of the energy flow diagrams shown in Figures 3–1 and 3–2 reveals a striking difference between the two ecosystems. In Root Spring most of the energy rich materials eaten by heterotrophs entered the system as plant debris, whereas in Silver Springs most of the heterotroph food was produced within the system by the autotrophs. This difference emphasizes the fact that some heterotrophs consume living plants and others feed on dead plant material. ODUM (1962) noted this feature and pointed out that two basic food chains are present in each ecosystem: *the grazing food chain*, consisting of the herbivores which feed on living plants together with their predators; and the *detritus food chain*, consisting of the herbivores which feed on dead plant material, with their predators. Functionally, the distinction between grazing and detritus food chains is of importance, for usually there is a considerable time lag between the direct consumption of living plants and the ultimate utilization of dead organic matter. It is therefore useful, in any analysis, to separate the two types of food chain.

Figure 3–3, modified after ODUM (1962, 1963), shows two composite energy flow models. In the marine ecosystem it is clear that the grazing chain is the major pathway of energy flow, whereas in the forest ecosystem the detritus chain is the more important.

The Odum models indicate that the two food chains are not completely isolated from one another. For instance, the dead bodies of animals that were once part of the grazing food chain become incorporated in the detritus chain, as do the faeces of the grazing chain animals.

The evidence at present available to us suggests that, in many ecosystems, the detritus or decomposer food chain is of greater importance in terms of energy flow than the grazing chain. In Silver Springs (Figure 3–2) for example, where the heterotroph food supply was initially present as living plants, there was a greater flow of energy through the decomposers (5,060 kcal/m²/yr) than through the grazers (3,368 kcal/m²/yr). The importance of the detritus chain should not be overlooked in any ecosystem.

3.3 Decomposers

The heterotrophs of the detritus food chain, that is the decomposers, constitute a more heterogeneous collection of organisms than those of the grazing chain. In terrestrial situations there are, amongst detritus feeders,

3

the relatively large organisms such as earthworms, woodlice, millipedes, toadstools; smaller forms such as mites (Acari), springtails (Collembola), and free-living round worms (Nematoda); also the micro-organisms (protozoa, fungi, and bacteria). The detritus food chains of aquatic habitats have their counterparts to these categories.

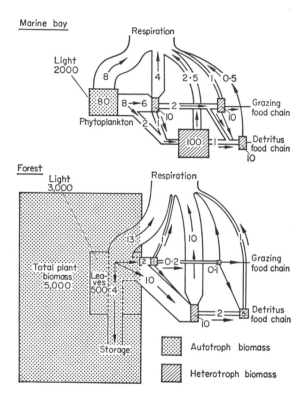

Fig. 3-3   Energy flow models for two contrasting types of ecosystem. Standing crop biomass in kcal/m², and energy flow in kcal/m²/day. (Adapted from ODUM, 1962.)

Currently it is thought that micro-organisms can account for as much as 90 per cent of the energy flow though an ecosystem. If this is so, then one may wonder whether other heterotrophs play a significant role. There is evidence to suggest that the part played by them is far greater than indicated by energy flow studies. EDWARDS and HEATH (1963) examined the role of soil animals in the breakdown of various leaves. They collected leaves of oak and beech, cut 2·5 cm discs from them and placed the discs in nylon mesh bags 10 cm × 7 cm. The bags were made

from different sized mesh nylon, the different sized meshes allowing only
certain organisms to enter the bag.

	Mesh size	Organisms with free entry
I	7·000 mm	All micro-organisms and invertebrates.
2	1·000 mm	All micro-organisms and invertebrates except earthworms.
3	0·500 mm	Only micro-organisms, mites, springtails, enchytraeids, and small invertebrates.
4	0·003 mm	Only micro-organisms.

Fifty leaf discs were placed in each bag and buried 2·5 cm deep in
newly cultivated soil. Every two months the bags were dug up and their
contents examined visually to determine the area of leaf that had disap-
peared. Leaf area was calculated by placing each disc between glass

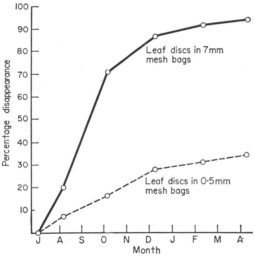

Fig. 3-4   Decomposition of oak leaf discs by soil animals. (Based on
EDWARDS and HEATH, 1963; courtesy of North Holland Publishing
Co., Amsterdam.)

plates; following this a perspex disc, of the same diameter as the original
leaf discs and marked with a grid of 100 squares, was placed over the leaf
disc and used to calculate the percentage loss of tissues. The results for
oak-leaf discs in 7 mm and 0·5 mm mesh bags are shown in Figure 3–4
and indicate that earthworms are important agents in breaking down
leaves. In the absence of earthworms breakdown was three times slower.

When 0·003 mm mesh bags were used, and animals other than micro-organisms were excluded, no visible breakdown of the leaf discs occurred during the nine months of investigation.

EDWARDS and HEATH's (1963) findings are of considerable interest when one recalls that micro-organisms are responsible for a large proportion of the energy flow in any ecosystem. It appears that the larger animals in some way facilitate the activity of micro-organisms. It is generally accepted that the larger heterotrophs by destroying litter mechanically provide, in the form of food remains and faeces, a substrate of small particles, and hence of large surface area, which can be attacked more readily by micro-organisms. What is not so clear is whether the larger heterotrophs alter the litter chemically as well as mechanically. NEF (1957), who reviewed leaf-litter breakdown, was of the opinion that soil animals not only fragment and mix leaf litter with soil but also cause chemical changes that enable bacteria and fungi to decompose it further. However, DUNGER (1958, 1960, and 1963) found with woodlice, millipedes, and certain lumbricid worms that the concentration of humin components in the litter was only little changed during its passage through the gut.

Clearly, further research is necessary before any general statement can be made.

Energy Flow at the Population Level

4

4.1 Individual organisms and ecosystems

It follows from the First Law of Thermodynamics that whatever quantity of energy enters an organism exactly the same amount, albeit in a different form, is ultimately surrendered by it. The same argument can be applied to whole ecosystems, for each is a functional unit and can therefore be considered an 'individual'. The results of the studies made on Root Spring and Silver Springs already reported and illustrated in Figures 3–1 and 3–2 clarify this point. Table 3 shows the relevant information.

Table 3 The fate of energy entering two spring ecosystems. (From data in ODUM (1956) and TEAL (1957)).

	Energy entering the ecosystem	All figures in kcal/m²/annum		
		Available energy dissipated in heat	Potential energy of protoplasm	Energy ultimately leaving the ecosystem
Silver Springs	410,486	408,986	2,500	410,486
Root Spring	3,060	2,185	901	3,086

In the Root Spring data the discrepancy of 26 kcal/m²/annum between the energy entering the ecosystem and that leaving the ecosystem can be accounted for on the grounds of experimental error.

Although the amount of energy ultimately leaving the ecosystem is equivalent to that entering it, it does so in a transformed state. In conformity with the Second Law of Thermodynamics energy is degraded from the free or high grade form (equivalent to work) to the bound or low grade form (equivalent to heat). Thus ecosystems, and indeed any systems that may be considered as units or 'individuals', behave from the thermodynamic viewpoint like individual organisms. The pathways of energy through any of these systems may be formally identified with the components of the Gibbs free energy equation (Wiegert, 1964)

$$\Delta H = \Delta F + T\Delta S$$

where ΔH (metabolizable energy) is the heat content (enthalpy) of the material assimilated by the system, or ingestion minus egestion;

ΔF (net energy) is the free energy actually available for the growth and maintenance (work) of the system;

$T\Delta S$ (specific dynamic action) is the heat increment, or energy degraded from a high grade form to a low grade form (heat) and not available for the growth and maintenance (work) of the system.

4.2   Limitations of the ecosystem approach

Without unlimited numbers of research workers a thermodynamic study of any living system must, of necessity, be restricted. An individual organism may be studied as a thermodynamic unit and no attention need be paid to the activities of its components (e.g. cells); similarly an ecosystem may be studied as a thermodynamic unit without attention to its components (e.g. species populations). Generally speaking, studies of energy flow through ecosystems do take into account the different trophic levels; but this approach, although a simplification, has the disadvantage that many animals are omnivorous and cannot be assigned to any one level.

The enormous task of studying energy flow both through, and within, a complex ecosystem restricts the research worker to an investigation of trophic levels as the components of the system, and the limitations of this approach will affect the overall study.

Certain species groups, such as earthworms in litter decomposition, play an important part in promoting energy flow, and it is important that some researches are directed towards elucidating the relative roles of species populations in ecosystems. Knowledge of the function of species populations will, together with information about individual organisms and complete ecosystems, afford man the opportunity of manipulating his natural environment without destroying it.

4.3   Plant population studies

Green plants are the main agents responsible for the manufacture of the high energy materials necessary for the maintenance of life. It is therefore important to know the efficiency with which various plant species convert the radiant energy of the sun into the chemical energy of plant protoplasm. This efficiency is referred to as *photosynthetic efficiency*. Care must be exercised in the use of this term, however, for a variety of 'photosynthetic efficiencies' may be calculated, depending upon whether radiant energy is taken to mean the total amount of light reaching the plants or only that absorbed by them and whether the plant protoplasm produced refers to gross or net production. Unfortunately the term photosynthetic efficiency has been applied to numerous ratios, but the one most used by ecologists is net production (total photosynthesis minus respiration) over the total amount of visible light reaching the plant (4,000 Å to 7,000 Å, the radiation wavelengths known to be utilized in photosynthesis). OVINGTON (1962) and HELLMERS (1964) quote several efficiencies of this type, some of which are shown in Table 4.

Table 4   The photosynthetic efficiency (ratio of net production to visible light energy received) of four plant communities. (From data in OVINGTON (1962) and HELLMERS (1964).)

Plant	Locality	Days in leaf	Photosynthetic efficiency
Scots pine	Britain	360	2·2 to 2·6
Sugar cane	Java	360	1·9
European beech	Denmark	164	2·5
Rice	Japan	150	2·2

In Table 4 photosynthetic efficiency (ratio of net production to the amount of visible light energy received) is based on the visible light energy received whilst the plants were in leaf. Clearly, if it was based on the incident visible radiation over the whole year, then the photosynthetic efficiencies of the deciduous plants would be lower than those recorded in Table 4. And also if the ratio gross production to incident visible light had been used in calculating the efficiencies then the figures would have been higher. BRAY (1961), for example, calculated a photosynthetic efficiency of 7·9 per cent for the conifer *Picea omorika*, by making allowances for reflected light, for light absorbed by non-chlorophyll-containing parts of the trees, and for material used in respiration. Similarly ODUM (1959) quotes a photosynthetic efficiency of 5 per cent for the producers in Silver Springs, Florida, when the efficiency is defined as the ratio of gross production over incident visible light.

The conclusions to be drawn from this account of photosynthetic efficiency may be summarized:

1. The term photosynthetic efficiency, unless carefully defined, is of limited value.
2. In natural populations of plants, photosynthetic efficiency, no matter how it is defined, is low and usually of the order of 1 to 5 per cent.

It is possible to increase the photosynthetic efficiency of plants, and this has been done in the case of mass culture of unicellular algae such as *Chlorella*. These algae can be grown in a stirred solution containing the requisite nutrient salts, and an optimum concentration of carbon dioxide. Provided that young cells are cultured in a low light intensity, efficiencies of 30 per cent can be achieved. However, a high photosynthetic efficiency does not mean that the amount of plant protoplasm produced per unit time is any greater than in plants with a lower efficiency. TAMIYA (1957) has shown that algal cultures with a high photosynthetic efficiency have a low productivity. Furthermore, when productivity is increased by means of higher light intensities efficiency falls to between 2 and 6 per cent, which is no better than in many natural plant populations.

ODUM (1956) pointed out that productivity rather than photosynthetic efficiency is more likely to be of importance to the survival of a plant population, and therefore selection of those systems with a high productivity is likely to occur. Indeed most ecologists, considering the conversion of solar radiation into plant protoplasm, express their findings as gross or net production rather than photosynthetic efficiency.

Productivity measurements over a short period of time, for example a day, rarely give much indication of the capacity of plants for sustained productivity. A year is well defined, and the variability of annual productivity is much less than for shorter periods, and most plant communities have natural periodicities related to the year. It is therefore desirable, whenever possible, to express productivity on an annual basis.

Two general methods of determining annual productivity exist. One is based on finding the average rate of photosynthesis throughout the year, and the other on studying the increase in biomass during a year's growth. The former relies on determinations of oxygen production or carbon dioxide consumption throughout the year, whereas the latter depends on the harvesting of the plant material at the end of the growing season, so that the photosynthetic rate can be deduced from changes in plant biomass. Direct measurement is most useful when the plants are subject to grazing losses whilst the harvest method can be used where grazing losses are negligible, and where there is a marked annual fluctuation in biomass. POMEROY (1961) has reviewed the various methods employed in measuring primary production.

WESTLAKE (1963) has compared annual productivity estimates for a variety of plant communities. Table 5 shows some of the estimates quoted by him.

A comparison of thirty-one different plant communities led WESTLAKE (1963) to the conclusion that the most productive communities, on an annual basis, occur in the tropics where rain forests and perennials under intensive cultivation may produce 50–80 metric tons/hectare in a year (where one hectare equals 10,000m^2 or 2·471 acres). In temperate regions the most productive communities appear to be fertile reedswamps which may produce 30–45 m t/ha.

These estimates of annual net primary production give us information about the relative productivity of different types of plant community. The net production per year is expressed as metric tons of organic (ash free) material per hectare, but given information about the calorific content of the different plant species it would be a simple matter, for the purpose of energy flow studies, to convert the figures into energy units.

Table 5 Estimates of the annual productivity of eleven plant communities. (After WESTLAKE (1963); courtesy of *Biol. Rev.*)

Region	Dominant species	Notes	Annual mean productivity organic (ash free) dry wt in mt/ha
Java	*Saccharum officinarum*	Sugar cane, a tropical perennial	87
Israel	*Zea mays*	Maize, cultivated annual	34
Germany	*Scirpus lacustris*	Club-rush in temperate reedswamps	46
Minnesota	*Typha* hybrid	Reedmace in temperate reedswamps	29
England	*Abies grandis*	Fir, temperate conifer	> 34
New Zealand	*Lolium* spp.	Grass, temperate	29
England	*Alnus incana*	Deciduous tree, temperate	> 15
Nova Scotia	*Laminaria longicuris*	Benthic marine alga, temperate	32
Marshall Islands	Green algae	Benthic algae of tropical reef	39
California	*Scenedesmus* sp.	Alga, with sewage treatment	45
Denmark	*Oscillatoria agardhii*	Blue-green alga of phytoplankton	1·4

In any event we do have estimates, for a number of plant populations, of the amount of metabolizable material made available to the heterotrophs every year.

We shall consider whether man's activities can be directed towards increasing the annual net production of different regions in Chapter 5; but in the next section we shall examine the ways in which primary production is used by animal populations.

4.4 Animal population studies

By procedures similar to those outlined in earlier sections it is possible to estimate the annual amount of plant material made available by a plant population, or community, to the heterotrophs in the same ecosystem. It now remains to consider the use to which this plant material is put by animal populations.

As shown in Chapter 3 the role of animals such as earthworms and millipedes in promoting energy flow through ecosystems is far greater than is suggested by a study of their metabolism, which is the only aspect dealt with in this section.

In the same way that Gibbs' free energy equation can be used to study individual animals, or whole ecosystems, it can also be applied to animal populations. As we have learned, this equation is expressed formally as:

$$\Delta H = \Delta F + T\Delta S$$

but for the purpose of studying the bioenergetics of animal populations we may write:

| Energy content of food assimilated | = | Energy content of tissues produced in growth and reproduction | + | Energy degraded and lost as heat of respiration |

Ideally a study of any animal population will attempt to solve the whole equation, but time often restricts the study to a single component. Respiratory metabolism has been most studied in small animals, whereas animals of importance to man as food have been investigated from the growth, or production, viewpoint.

Before considering detailed studies of the metabolism of animal populations it will be useful to examine some of the wider aspects of respiratory metabolism, for it is in this sphere that the value of comparative studies is clearly indicated. MACFADYEN (1963) compared the total annual respiration of nine soil types, and some of his diagrams are reproduced in Figure 4–1. The examples chosen are all beech forests, and it should be noted that two major soil types are being compared: *mor*, the peaty humus formed in leached soils; and *mull*, the fertile leaf mould typically associated with fertile forest soils.

It seems reasonable to suppose that the quality of plant material produced by a beech forest on a mull soil will not differ markedly from that produced by a beech forest on a mor soil, although the total quantities produced per annum may differ. If this is so, then it is of interest to note that the total annual respiration of the three beech forests in Figure 4–1 not only differs between sites, but that the proportional contribution of the different trophic groups to this total varies from site to site. It is clear that large decomposers such as millipedes, woodlice, and lumbricid worms make only a small contribution to the total annual respiration of mor soils, whilst in mull soils their contribution is large. In mor soils the small decomposers such as nematode and enchytraeid worms, mites, and springtails compensate for the absence of large

Fig. 4–1 Comparison of the total annual respiration of three beech forest soils. The areas of the circles represent the total annual metabolism in kcal/m², and the areas of the sectors are proportional to the rates for each of the trophic groups. (After MACFADYEN, 1963; courtesy of North Holland Publishing Co., Amsterdam.)

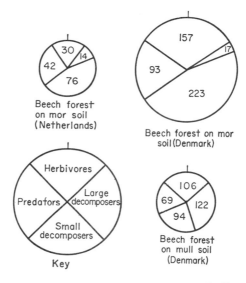

Beech forest on mor soil (Netherlands)

Beech forest on mor soil (Denmark)

Beech forest on mull soil (Denmark)

Key

decomposers. Clearly, from the viewpoint of respiratory metabolism small decomposers in mor soils have a similar function in their ecosystem to that of large decomposers in mull soils.

For the purpose of understanding and comparing the functioning of different ecosystems the contribution of individual species populations to the total annual respiration of the ecosystem should be investigated.

Studies of the metabolic activity of species populations are not numerous, although increasing attention is being paid to such matters. BORNEBUSCH (1930) estimated biomass, and respiratory activity, for a number of animal populations in a variety of forest soils, but the inadequacy of his census methods underestimated the total numbers of the smaller animals. Recently more accurate figures have been made available.

NIELSEN (1961) and O'CONNOR (1963) have made detailed investigations of the respiratory metabolism of soil-dwelling enchytraeid worms. Following population studies, the respiratory rates of different sized enchytraeids were investigated in the laboratory by means of a Cartesian diver respirometer (HOLTER, 1943), a technique which enables the oxygen consumption of very small animals to be measured.

Figure 4–2, taken from O'CONNOR, shows that oxygen consumption per unit weight declines steeply with increasing live weight. It also shows that different species have different respiratory rates; this is because some species are more active than others. For this reason it is useful to combine

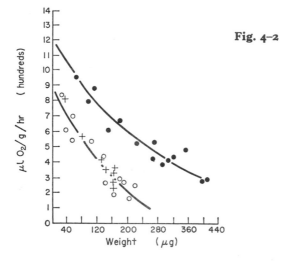

Fig. 4–2 The relationship between oxygen consumption and live weight for three species of enchytraeid worm, *Cognettia cognettia* (●), *Marionina cambrensis* (+), and *Achaeta eiseni* (○). (After O'CONNOR, 1963; courtesy of North Holland Publishing Co., Amsterdam.)

population estimates with respiratory rate information and compare the annual levels of population density and metabolism for each of the species studied. It is clear from Table 6 that *Cognettia*, though least important numerically, ranks second in order of biomass, and has the highest population metabolism.

Table 6   Summary of annual levels of population density, biomass, metabolism. (After O'CONNOR, 1963.)

Species	Mean density	Biomass	Metabolic activity	
	$(10^3/m^2)$	(g/m^2)	$(l.O_2/m^2/yr)$	$(kcal/m^2/yr)$
Marionina	68·7	5·512	12·4	59·2
Cognettia	30·9	3·667	13·5	64·5
Achaeta	34·7	1·615	5·4	25·8

The importance of studying individual species populations has been emphasized, amongst others, by BERTHET (1963). Working with adult oribatid mites Berthet calculated the metabolic activity of forty-six different species populations and showed that respiratory activity varied from species to species. PHILLIPSON (1960a, 1960b, 1962, and 1963) has shown that not only do species differ in their metabolic activity but that life stages within a single species also vary. Figure 4–3 shows the oxygen consumption per unit weight for different life stages of the harvest spider *Leiobunum rotundum* and illustrates intra-specific variability. The high oxygen consumption of small individuals is clear, as is the increase in respiratory rate of animals (particularly females) weighing 3–8 mg. Also noteworthy is the high respiratory rate of October males (mean weight = 14·5 mg) and October females (mean weight = 23·2 mg). A high oxygen uptake per unit weight is expected of small individuals, the increased

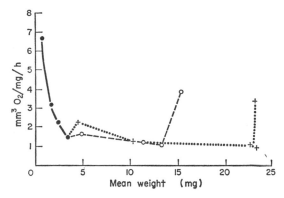

Fig. 4–3 The relationship between oxygen consumption and live weight in the harvest spider *Leiobunum rotundum*, unsexed individuals (●), males (○), females (+). (From PHILLIPSON, 1963; courtesy of *Oikos*.)

rate between 3–8 mg can be attributed to a greater metabolic activity associated with developing eggs, for, as shown by dissection, increase in ovary weight was most rapid between 2–10 mg body weight. October is the month when most *Leiobunum rotundum* die off and the high respiratory activity in this month is probably due to metabolic inefficiency associated with senescence. This intra-specific variability, although not much studied as yet, is probably more widespread than is generally realized. For example, in addition to harvest spiders it has recently been shown to hold for the wood louse, *Oniscus asellus* (PHILLIPSON and WATSON, in press). The inference is clear; if respiratory data are to be used in conjunction with population data to calculate population metabolism, then it is essential that measurements of metabolic activity be made on all life stages of a single species, throughout the course of a year. Further, because temperature influences metabolic rate it is desirable to measure respiratory rate at the same temperature as the natural environment, although in certain circumstances it is possible to apply a correction factor (KROGH, 1916). Finally, whenever possible, measurements of respiratory rate should be taken over a period exceeding 24 h thereby counteracting differential respiratory rates due to either diurnal or nocturnal activity. Table 7 shows the day/night oxygen consumption of: (a) *Mitopus morio*, a harvest spider which is almost equally active day and night; and (b) *Oligolophus tridens*, another harvest spider slightly more nocturnal than *Mitopus*.

Table 7   Day/night oxygen consumption of two harvest spiders. Levels of significance (P) are shown in parentheses. (After PHILLIPSON (1962); courtesy of *Oikos*.)

	Day	Night
	mm³ O₂/mg/h	mm³ O₂/mg/h
Mitopus morio	0·626 (0·001)	0·796
Oligolophus tridens	0·943 (0·01)	1·375

   Studies of the respiratory metabolism of populations are in their early stages, but no doubt the coming decade will see great advances made.
   Investigations of ΔF in the Gibbs free energy equation, that is the growth of animal populations from the viewpoint of productivity, have been largely restricted to fish of commercial importance. One of the most frequently quoted studies is that of ALLEN (1951), who investigated the production of brown trout (*Salmo trutta*) in a 7½ mile stretch of the River Horokiwi in New Zealand. The total number of trout eggs laid in a single season was calculated by two independent methods.

1. By estimating the number of ripe females present in the river by means of a seine net sampling programme and multiplying this number by the mean number of eggs present in a ripe female.
2. By counting the number of redds in which the eggs were laid and

Table 8   Production of *Salmo trutta* in Horokiwi Stream. (From MACAN (1963) after ALLEN; courtesy of Longmans, Green and Co., and of the original publishers, E. Schweizbart'sche Verlagsbuchhandlung, Stuttgart.)

Age	0	6	12	18	24	30	-months
Number	1,000	15	7	4	2	1	-fish
Wt of a single fish	1/250	2	6	9	12	16	-oz
Wt of all living fish	¼	1¾	2½	2¼	1½	1	-lb
Wt of all fish that have died	0	3¾	5½	7	8¼	9	-lb
Total weight of fish produced	¼	5½	8	9¼	9¾	10	-lb

Table 9 The utilization of energy ($\Delta H = \Delta F + T\Delta S$) by different animal populations.

Species	Status	Assimilation (ΔH) kcal/m²/yr	Growth (ΔF) kcal/m²/yr	Respiration ($T\Delta S$) kcal/m²/yr	$\dfrac{\text{Respiration}}{\text{growth}}$	Authority
Invertebrates						
Modiolus demissus (ribbed mussel)	Filter feeding poikilotherm	56·0	17·0	39·0	2·3	KUENZLER, 1961
Orthoptera (various grasshoppers)	Herbivorous poikilotherms	25·6	4·0	21·6	5·4	ODUM, CONNELL, & DAVENPORT, 1962
Vertebrates						
Rutilus rutilus (roach)	Mainly herbivorous poikilotherm	119·0	8·6	110·0	12·8	MANN, 1964
Alburnus alburnus (bleak)	Mainly carnivorous poikilotherm	159·0	11·5	147·0	12·8	MANN, 1964
Mustela rixosa (least weasel)	Carnivorous homoiotherm	0·556	0·013	0·543	41·8	GOLLEY, 1960
Peromyscus polionotus (old-field mouse)	Granivorous homoiotherm	6·7	0·12	6·57	54·8	ODUM, CONNELL, & DAVENPORT, 1962
Passerculus sandwichensis (Savannah sparrow)	Granivorous homoiotherm	3·6	0·04	3·55	88·8	ODUM, CONNELL, & DAVENPORT, 1962

multiplying this number by the mean number of eggs per redd. In this way a reasonably accurate estimate of the number of eggs laid was obtained.

Further observation enabled the number of young hatched out to be calculated, this amounted to 500,000 in October, 1940. Subsequent sampling, and a programme of weighing and tagging the captured fish before returning them to the river, enabled estimates of population size and growth to be made. Table 8 summarizes the results; note that they are presented for one thousand newly hatched fish, and so for the 1940 year class (i.e. those fish hatched in 1940) the results should be multiplied by five hundred.

At the end of one year, for every one thousand young hatched, 8 lb of fish were produced of which 2½ lb were still alive. After one further year only 2 lb more fish flesh were produced, giving a total production of 9¾ lb, of which only 1½ lb still survived. Clearly man will receive his best returns of fish from the Horokiwi if he settles for the relatively small, one-year-old, 6 oz individuals.

A full evaluation of the free energy equation as applied to animal populations has been attempted on relatively few occasions. Table 9 summarizes some of the results currently available.

Although it is scientifically unsound to infer too much from the little data given in Table 9 it is interesting to speculate a little. For example, the proportions of assimilated food used in growth and respiration do not appear to be correlated with the body size or feeding habits of the individuals of the species populations studied. It does seem, however, that homoiotherms, in contrast with poikilotherms, use a greater proportion of their assimilated energy in respiration. This is probably due to the necessity of maintaining a steady body temperature by converting high grade energy to low grade energy. If it is generally true that poikilotherms build a greater proportion of their assimilated energy into body tissues than do homoiotherms, then from the point of view of man's efficient utilization of energy resources in the form of animal protein, it would be economically advantageous to man if poikilotherms were his major source of animal protein.

However, before any general statement can be made, further research on the bioenergetics of animal populations is clearly necessary and, as MCNAB (1963) has pointed out, a comparative study of the economics of poikilothermy and homoiothermy is to be strongly recommended.

Man and Balanced Ecosystems

5.1 The human population explosion and the need for food

The ever-increasing population requires the rational exploitation of the world's limited natural resources, and nowhere is the need more pressing than in food production. In a world where millions are permanently undernourished (see Figure 5–1) and where the total population increases exponentially, it is vital to discover how biological productivity can be used in the service of man without permanently reducing that productivity.

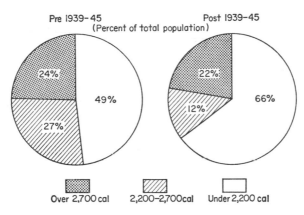

Pre 1939-45   Post 1939-45
(Percent of total population)

24% 49% 22% 66%

27% 12%

Over 2,700 cal 2,200–2,700cal Under 2,200 cal

Fig. 5–1 Distribution of the world population according to average daily supply of calories. (From HUXLEY, 1957; courtesy of the original publishers, Allen & Unwin.)

5.2 Plants as a source of food

Throughout this book attention has been drawn to the facts that the primary source of energy for living organisms is the sun and that only green plants can utilize this energy to build up the complex organic compounds required by animals as food. Under natural conditions between 1 and 5 per cent only of the total incident visible light is converted by plants into the chemical energy of plant protoplasm. And it is clear that animals in building up their body tissues, which may serve as food for man, dissipate a large proportion of the chemical energy of plant protoplasm as heat. Thus for man to make the maximum use of the solar energy trapped by plants he should become mainly herbivorous.

If such a situation should arise it would be advantageous to know the potential primary productivity of ecosystems in all parts of the world.

ODUM (1959) has indicated the general pattern of the world distribution of primary production, and his schematic representation is reproduced in Figure 5–2. Agricultural crops, with the exception of all-the-year-round crops such as sugar cane, can be seen to have a lower primary productivity than a number of natural ecosystems. Given good soil structure, ample nutrients, and water, many natural ecosystems utilize fully the available incident solar radiation. This becomes possible when there is a full photosynthetically active plant cover throughout the growing season, and often throughout the year, which traps the maximum amount of sunlight —a condition rarely achieved with agricultural crops. One has only to

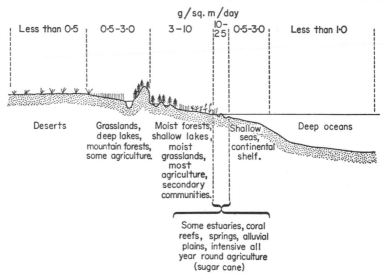

Fig. 5–2   World distribution of primary production. (Redrawn from ODUM, 1959; courtesy of W. B. Saunders, Philadelphia.)

think of the bare patches of earth between young crop plants to realize that much solar radiation of potential use in photosynthesis is wasted. There are technical difficulties of planting and harvesting to overcome, but here is a case for the growing of mixed crops, which together give a full plant cover.

An exception among crops is sugar cane, and in the tropics daily sunshine throughout the year is probably the reason why it shows such high productivity when compared with the agricultural crops of more temperate regions. The effect of solar radiation on plant productivity is shown by BRAY and GORHAM's (1964) figures for the annual production of forest litter in different parts of the world (see Figure 5–3).

In deserts, for example, maximum utilization of solar radiation is limited by lack of water and mineral nutrients rather than by agricultural practices. In such circumstances irrigation and the addition of fertilizers will do much to increase primary productivity. Intensive horticultural practice where artificial methods of heating and lighting increase the length of the growing season in the cooler areas of the earth is yet another means of raising productivity above the normal level.

Some natural ecosystems do have a higher productivity than man-made systems under similar climatic conditions, which suggests that agricultural crops have not here achieved their full production potential. Increased understanding of the functioning of natural ecosystems may indicate the means by which the full potential might be achieved and sustained. Clearly, the production per unit area of the majority of man's

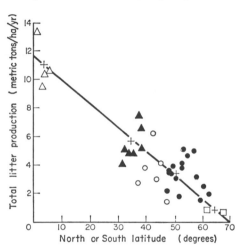

Fig. 5-3   Annual production of total litter in relation to latitude, equatorial (△), warm temperate (▲), cool temperate North American (○), cool temperate European (●), and Arctic-Alpine (□). (From BRAY and GORHAM, 1964; courtesy of *Adv. Ecol. Res.*)

traditional crops is uneconomic in the maximum utilization of solar energy; plants not normally used as a food source might prove more efficient than the traditional crops.

PIRIE (1962) has shown that protein extracted from plant material such as tree leaves is as good as or better than fish meal. Such protein could be incorporated into palatable foodstuffs for direct use by human beings, or it could be used as food material for man's domestic animals. Protein extraction on a commercial scale from forest and agricultural waste deserves serious consideration, and it might be extended to include many kinds of highly productive natural vegetation.

Under any cropping regime a sustained annual yield is essential if the system is to be of permanent value. The greatest chance of obtaining a sustained maximum yield probably lies in a detailed knowledge of the energy and nutrient flow both through, and within, the undisturbed natural ecosystem. Such knowledge provides a yardstick by means of which it will be possible to assess the effect of man's interference on the productivity of the area being exploited, and thus indicate when and where corrective steps should be taken to prevent the overexploiting of our natural resources.

5.3 Animals as a source of food

It is unlikely that mankind will ever become solely herbivorous, and it is necessary to consider the means by which adequate animal protein can be produced for his use. As MACFADYEN (1964) has indicated, the crops which produce the highest calorific yield are those most deficient in proteins, and yet the human diet requires about 20 g of protein per 1,000 kcal. Thus at the present time there is a need to encourage the production of animal food.

The concept of a constant ecological efficiency of 10 per cent presupposes that for every 1,000 calories of plant material consumed by herbivores only 100 calories are passed on to carnivores, and of these a mere 10 calories reach the top carnivores. These simple facts are the reason why the number of links in any one food chain rarely exceeds five, and account for the general form of pyramids of energy.

In the event of man remaining an omnivore the most economic use of solar energy, when converted to the chemical energy of animal protein, is the consumption of herbivore flesh. In this way the wasteful dissipation of herbivore chemical energy as heat by carnivores other than man will be avoided. The majority of man's domestic food animals are, in fact, herbivorous.

On the assumption that gross ecological efficiency is of the order of 10 per cent then, on average, animals convert approximately 10 per cent of their food intake to growth. It is known, however, that individual gross growth efficiencies

$$\left(\frac{\text{calories of growth}}{\text{calories consumed}} \right)$$

vary from 6 to 37 per cent, and net growth efficiencies

$$\left(\frac{\text{calories of growth}}{\text{calories assimilated}} \right)$$

from 5 to 60 per cent. The aim of converting as much solar energy as possible into animal protein for human use may be served best by cropping those herbivores with the highest growth efficiencies. A high net growth efficiency indicates that a relatively small amount of the assimilated energy is lost as heat of respiration and that the remainder is used for growth; whereas a high gross growth efficiency points to efficient assimilation of food energy for growth, little being voided as faeces or used in respiration.

Growth efficiencies of beef cattle raised on grassland are of the order of 10·9 per cent net and 4·1 per cent gross; not particularly high ratios when compared with *Daphnia*, which according to ARMSTRONG (1960) has a gross growth efficiency of 4 to 13 per cent and a net growth efficiency of 55 to 59 per cent. If man's sole aim was to obtain the maximum conversion of solar energy into animal protein then *Daphnia* would prove a better food animal than beef cattle. But high growth efficiencies are not the only desirable herbivore qualities; in addition to the food preferences of man there is the need for a product which can be cropped with ease, and domestic farm animals belong to this category.

The traditional methods of rearing livestock are not the most economic means of producing animal protein. As MACFADYEN (1964) has pointed out, beef cattle raised on grassland consume only one-seventh of the total primary production, the remainder being consumed by other herbivores and decomposers of no direct food value to man. By minimizing the amount of plant material consumed by the herbivores and decomposers and maximizing that reaching the cattle the yield of beef per unit area could, in theory, be raised to seven times its present level. Modern methods of animal husbandry do maximize the amount of food energy reaching the animals, obvious examples being strip grazing, the production of eggs by battery hens, and the raising of calves, chickens, and pigs in specially constructed buildings such as broiler houses. Except in the case of strip grazing, plant material is harvested, processed, and brought to the animals thereby reducing the proportion of the total plant material available to the decomposers of the natural ecosystem. The use of processed foods also permits the feeding of plant materials not normally used as a food source to domestic farm animals. Clearly, the yield of animal protein per unit area of vegetation can be increased several fold by intensive farming practices.

A combination of high individual growth efficiency and the maximization of food energy reaching the livestock is the most efficient way yet of producing the animal protein traditionally eaten by man. This principle is followed in raising broiler chickens and calves. It is well known that growth efficiencies of the young are higher than in older animals. For example the gross growth efficiencies of young beef cattle and young chickens are of the order of 35 per cent, as compared with the mean value of 4 to 5 per cent shown over their whole life histories. To raise livestock beyond the age of maximum growth efficiency, usually prior to the attainment of reproductive age, is wasteful in terms of food production for man. In chickens, gross growth efficiency declines markedly 3 to 4 months after hatching and at this age chickens should be killed for meat. In practice this is how the broiler industry operates. Hens do not lay eggs until 5 to 6 months old, when growth efficiency has declined, and to keep hens for egg production is a wasteful method of producing food for man. Kleiber (1961) has shown that if man met all his food requirements with free range eggs it would require 7·4 acres per man per year to achieve this as compared with 0·3 acres to feed a man for a year on grain, or 0·002 acres if algae were used as food.

The principles employed in the broiler industry can be, and are, applied to all forms of livestock raised for the meat market. This type of intensive farming does, of course, raise other problems (aesthetic and moral), but such considerations are beyond the scope of this book.

Given ample supplies of plant food the production of animal protein per unit time, as well as per unit area of vegetation, can be increased. This can be achieved by employing intensive farming methods for those

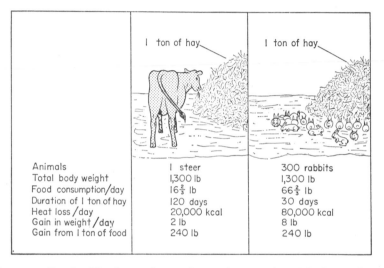

Animals	1 steer	300 rabbits
Total body weight	1,300 lb	1,300 lb
Food consumption/day	$16\frac{2}{3}$ lb	$66\frac{2}{3}$ lb
Duration of 1 ton of hay	120 days	30 days
Heat loss/day	20,000 kcal	80,000 kcal
Gain in weight/day	2 lb	8 lb
Gain from 1 ton of food	240 lb	240 lb

Fig. 5–4   Food utilization and rate of growth per unit weight by cattle and rabbits. (Based on KLEIBER, 1961; courtesy of John Wiley and Sons.)

animals which possess high growth efficiencies and high growth rates. Figure 5–4 adapted from KLEIBER (1961), illustrates this point particularly well.

From a given amount of hay, rabbits produce the same quantity of meat as beef cattle, but they do so four times as quickly, and therefore in terms of meat production per unit time rabbits are much more efficient than beef cattle.

In certain countries, for example, East Africa, European livestock has long been a familiar sight, and the fact that cattle-raising has encountered formidable difficulties with diseases such as trypanosomiasis and rinderpest has not deterred farmers from raising 'European meat'. It is now known that native animals such as zebra and antelope are relatively immune to the diseases which affect European cattle, and they do not damage their habitat to the same extent as introduced species. Furthermore they have a higher productivity. Under such circumstances increasing use is being made of range animals for human food, great care being taken to exploit them in a rational manner. In this instance evolutionary processes have made nature a more efficient producer of animal protein than man.

Another traditional source of animal protein for man is fish. At the beginning of this century it was held that whatever fish man took from the sea would be but a trifling loss compared with mortality from other causes, and thus there was no need to 'ration' fishing. Today we know only too well how easy it is to over-fish with very serious consequences. On occasions when fish such as plaice have been tagged and returned to the sea, some 40 per cent of the marked fish have later been recaptured. If this is taken to indicate the normal proportion of a population fished, the tremendous power of modern fishing is shown. There is evidence that many areas are being fished beyond their limit, thus depleting the stocks of fish and severely upsetting the balance of nature. For example GRAHAM (1943) quotes figures for two relatively stable periods of fishing; in 1909–13 fish, other than herring, taken from the North Sea amounted to 434,000 tons; in 1929–32, with all the improvements in fishing gear and effort the catch totalled 428,000 tons. Clearly, unlimited fisheries become inefficient fisheries in terms of adequate return for effort. Nowhere is this more apparent than in the whaling industry. One of the major problems facing fisheries scientists today is the discovery of the limit at which a maximum sustained yield of fish can be obtained for the minimum of fishing effort. Obviously detailed knowledge about the numbers and habits of fish is necessary, and this requires in turn knowledge of the organisms on which they live and hence the energy and nutrient relationships of the whole marine ecosystem. With detailed information it may be possible to increase the productivity of certain parts of the sea. In the Kattegat, fish consume only 1 to 2 per cent of the standing crop of fish food, the remainder being eaten by invertebrate predators (THORSON, 1958); the problem here is to ensure that fish get a larger share of the available food. HARDY (1959) has asked if future farmers of the sea will be able to eradicate some of the invertebrate predators and so step up the quantity of fish carried in a given area? If this is to be done without upsetting the balance of nature, knowledge of the functioning of nature is essential.

Attempts have been made in more localized areas to increase fish productivity. For example, during the Second World War artificial fertilizers, in the form of super phosphate and sodium nitrate, added to a small area of the sea, Loch Craiglin in Scotland, increased the density of phytoplankton from 1,600 organisms per cu mm to 8,000 per cu mm over a 2 month period. Within a year an increase of 215 per cent in the bottom fauna was apparent, this despite the fact that approximately 25,000 young flounders and plaice had been introduced into the loch. Further, in less than 2 years the introduced fish had completed growth that they would have taken 5 to 6 years to make in their original home.

The speed with which fertilizers were absorbed makes it possible to visualize the practicality of farming our inshore waters. In the United Kingdom the White Fish Authority is currently investigating the artificial rearing of commercially important fish; this procedure will reduce normal predation losses and allow young healthy fish to be transplanted on a large scale to areas rich in fish food, areas which may be naturally productive such as the Dogger Bank or artificially fertilized regions similar to Loch Craiglin.

Many of the countries of the world are some distance from the sea. In such countries fresh water fish form an important source of animal

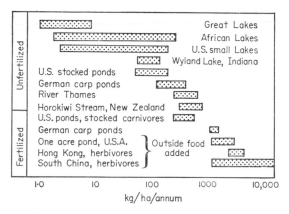

Fig. 5–5   Yield of fish obtained by man from different types of fresh water body. (Based on MANN, 1965; courtesy of *J. Anim. Ecol.*)

protein. The fish may be obtained from natural waters such as lakes and rivers by normal fishing methods or may be 'farmed' in managed fish ponds. Examples of natural fresh water fisheries are to be found in the American Great Lakes or the larger African lakes; here the problems facing the fisheries scientists are similar to those presented by sea fisheries. Managed fish ponds are much more obviously under man's control, and fish farms are to be found in many parts of the world. Good fish farm management aims at increasing to a maximum the primary productivity of the ponds, usually by applying fertilizers, and thereby creating a food energy reserve which can be utilized either directly or indirectly by the introduced fish population. As one might expect from the earlier discussion on the efficient utilization of food energy by terrestrial herbivores, herbivorous fish give a greater yield than carnivorous ones. Figure 5–5 adapted from MANN (1965) shows the yields of fish obtained from different fresh water bodies, and indicates how management can raise the yield to man above that obtained from natural waters. It is right to point out, however, that in those ponds giving the highest yield extra food was added, the food thus represents energy fixed in some place other than the fish pond. The transportation of food grown in one area to be fed to animals in yet another area suggests, as in the case of intensive animal husbandry, the possibility of using plants of no current commercial importance as a source of fish food.

There are sources of animal protein other than fish taken from aquatic habitats, the shellfish industry is not an insignificant one but is not as fully exploited as it could be, particularly in view of the fact that the net growth efficiency of bivalve molluscs is higher than that of most vertebrates (see Table 4).

Many animals both terrestrial and aquatic are at present of no commercial value to man and are often considered to be pests, for example starfish, the well-known predators of oysters. How long will it be before man upsets even further the functioning of natural ecosystems by putting to his use the currently non-commercial organisms? HARDY (1959) has, amongst other things, suggested the use of starfish when removed from oyster beds as poultry feed, an excellent idea. Indeed many of the ideas put forward for possible uses of our natural resources are excellent, but one must always remember that interference by man usually results in an upset in the balance of nature. An upsetting of this kind means interference in the pattern of energy flow through the ecosystem. One of the ways of ensuring rational exploitation of a natural resource and guarding against permanent imbalance is to know and understand the pattern of energy flow through the system both before and after man's interference; herein lies the value of ecological energetics.

References

ALLEN, K. R. (1951). *New Zealand Marine Dept. Fish. Bull.*, **10**, 1–238

ARMSTRONG, J. (1960). The Dynamics of *Dugesia tigrina* Populations and of *Daphnia pulex* Populations as modified by Immigration, Ph.D. Dissertation, Department of Zoology, University of Michigan, Ann Arbor

BERTHET, P. (1963). Mesure de la Consommation d'Oxygène des Oribatides (Acariens) de la Litière des Forêts. In *Soil Organisms*, edited by J. DOEKSEN and J. VAN DER DRIFT. North-Holland Publishing Co., Amsterdam

BORNEBUSCH, C. H. (1930). *Det. forstl. Forsogsv. i Danmark*, **11**, 1–244

BRAY, J. R. (1961). *Plant Physiol.*, **36**, 371–3

BRAY, J. R. and GORHAM, E. (1964). *Adv. Ecol. Res.*, **2**, 101–57

DEMPSTER, J. P. (1960). *J. Anim. Ecol.*, **29**, 149–67

DOWDESWELL, W. H. (1959). *Practical Animal Ecology*, Methuen and Co. Ltd., London

DUNGER, W. (1958). *Ztschr. Pflanzenern. Düng. Bodenkunde.*, **82**, 174–93

DUNGER, W. (1960). *Zentral. Bakt. Parasit. Infektionskr. Hyg.*, **113**, 345–55

DUNGER, W. (1963). Leistungsspezifität bei Streuzersetzern. In *Soil Organisms*. Edited by J. DOEKSEN and J. VAN DER DRIFT. North-Holland Publishing Co., Amsterdam

EDWARDS, C. A. and HEATH, G. W. (1963). The Role of Soil Animals in Breakdown of Leaf Material. In *Soil Organisms*, edited by J. DOEKSEN and J. VAN DER DRIFT. North-Holland Publishing Co., Amsterdam

ELTON, C. (1927). *Animal Ecology*, Sidgwick and Jackson Ltd., London

ENGELMANN, M. D. (1961). *Ecol. Monogr.*, **16**, 221–38

FOX, H. M. and WINGFIELD, C. A. (1938). *J. exp. Biol.*, **15**, 437–45

FRASER, J. H. (1962). *Nature Adrift*, G. T. Foulis and Co. Ltd., London

GOLLEY, F. B. (1960). *Ecol. Monogr.*, **30**, 187–206

GRAHAM, M. (1943). *The Fish Gate*, Faber and Faber Ltd., London

HARDY, A. C. (1924). *Fish. Invest. Lond. Ser. II*, **7**, No. 3, 53 pp.

HARDY, SIR A. C. (1959). *The Open Sea: II, Fish and Fisheries*. Collins Co. Ltd., London

HELLMERS, H. (1964). *Quart. Rev. Biol.*, **39**, 249–57

HOLTER, H. (1943). *C. R. Trav. Lab. Carlsberg, Ser. chim.*, **24**, 399–478

HUXLEY, SIR J. S. (1957). *New Bottles for New Wine*, Chatto and Windus Ltd., London

IVLEV, V. S. (1934). *Biochem. Ztschr.*, **275**, 49–55

JONES, J. R. E. (1949). *J. Anim. Ecol.*, **18**, 142–59

JUDAY, C. (1940). *Ecology*, **21**, 438–50

KLEIBER, M. (1961). *The Fire of Life*, Wiley and Sons, New York

KUENZLER, E. J. (1961). *Limnol. Oceanogr.*, **6**, 191–204

LINDEMANN, R. L. (1942). *Ecology*, **23**, 399–418

MACAN, T. T. (1963). *Freshwater Ecology*, Longmans, Green and Co., London

MACFADYEN, A. (1963). The Contribution of the Microfauna to the Total Soil Metabolism. In *Soil Organisms*, edited by J. DOEKSEN and J. VAN DER DRIFT, North-Holland Publishing Co., Amsterdam

MACFADYEN, A. (1964). Energy Flow in Ecosystems and its Exploitation by Grazing. In *Grazing in Terrestrial and Marine Environments*, edited by D. J. CRISP. Blackwell Scientific Publications, Oxford

MCNAB, B. K. (1963). *Ecology*, **44**, 521–32

MANN, K. H. (1964). *Verh. Internat. Verein. Limnol.*, **15**, 485–95

MANN, K. H. (1965). *J. Anim. Ecol.*, **34**, 253–75

NEF, L. (1957). *Agricultura, Louvain*, **5**, 245–316

NIELSEN, C. O. (1961). *Oikos*, **12**, 17–35

O'CONNOR, F. B. (1963). Oxygen Consumption and Population Metabolism of Enchytraeidae. In *Soil Organisms* edited by J. DOEKSEN and J. VAN DER DRIFT. North-Holland Publishing Co., Amsterdam

ODUM, E. P. (1959). *Fundamentals of Ecology*, 2nd ed., W. B. Saunders Co., Philadelphia

ODUM, E. P. (1962). *Japanese Journal of Ecology*, **12**, 108–18

ODUM, E. P. (1963). *Ecology*, Holt, Rinehart and Winston, New York

ODUM, E. P., CONNELL, C. E., and DAVENPORT, L. B. (1962). *Ecology*, **43**, 88–96

ODUM, E. P., and KUENZLER, E. J. (1963). Experimental Isolation of Food Chains in an Old-Field Ecosystem with the Use of Phosphorus-32. In *Radioecology*, edited by V. SCHULTZ and A. W. KLEMENT JR. Reinhold Publ. Corp., New York

ODUM, H. T. (1956). *Ecology*, **37**, 592–97

ODUM, H. T. (1957). *Ecol. Monogr.*, **27**, 55–112

ODUM, H. T., and ODUM, E. P. (1955). *Ecol. Monogr.*, **25**, 291–320

OVINGTON, J. D. (1962). *Adv. Ecol. Res.*, **1**, 103–92

PHILLIPSON, J. (1960a). *J. Anim. Ecol.*, **29**, 35–43

PHILLIPSON, J. (1960b). *J. Anim. Ecol.*, **29**, 299–307

PHILLIPSON, J. (1962). *Oikos*, **13**, 311–22

PHILLIPSON, J. (1963). *Oikos*, **14**, 212–23

PHILLIPSON, J. (1964). *Oikos*, **15**, 130–39

PHILLIPSON, J. and WATSON, J. (in press)

PIRIE, N. W. (1962). *J. R. statist. Soc. Ser. A*, **125**, 399–417

POMEROY, L. R. (1961). Productivity and How to Measure It. In *Algae and Metropolitan Wastes*. U.S. Department of Health, Education, and Welfare, Public Health Service, Robert A. Taft Sanitary Engineering Center, Cincinatti

PORTER, G. (1965). *The Laws of Disorder*. British Broadcasting Corporation, London

REYNOLDSON, T. B. and YOUNG, J. O. (1963). *J. Anim. Ecol.*, **32**, 175–91

RICHMAN, S. (1958). *Ecol. Monogr.*, **28**, 273–91

SLOBODKIN, L. B. (1959). *Ecology*. **40**, 232–43

SLOBODKIN, L. B. (1962). *Adv. Ecol. Res.*, **1**, 69–101

SLOBODKIN, L. B. (1964). *J. Anim. Ecol.*, 33 (Suppl.), 131–48

SLOBODKIN, L. B. and RICHMAN, S. (1960). *Ecology*, **41**, 784–85

TAMIYA, H. (1957). *Ann. Rev. Plant Physiol.*, **8**, 309–34

TEAL, J. M. (1957). *Ecol. Monogr.*, **27**, 283–302

THORSON, G. (1958). Parallel Level-Bottom Communities, Their Temperature Adaptation, and their 'Balance' between Predators and Food Animals. In *Perspectives in Marine Biology*, edited by A. A. BUZZATI-TRAVERSO. University of California Press, Berkeley

WESTLAKE, D. F. (1963). *Biol. Rev.*, **38**, 385–425

WIEGERT, R. G. (1964). *Ecol. Monogr.*, **34**, 217–241

YOUNG, J. O., MORRIS, I. G., and REYNOLDSON, T. B. (1964). *Arch. Hydrobiol.*, **60**, 366–73